Constructivist Views on the Teaching and Learning of Mathematics

Constructivist Views on the Teaching and Learning of Mathematics

edited by

Robert B. Davis
Carolyn A. Maher
Nel Noddings

NATIONAL COUNCIL OF TEACHERS OF MATHEMATICS

1906 Association Drive, Reston, Virginia 20191-1502
703-620-9840; (800) 235-7566; www.nctm.org

Fifth printing 2004

Library of Congress Cataloging-in-Publication Data:

Constructivist views on the teaching and learning of mathematics/
edited by Robert B. Davis, Carolyn A. Maher, Nel Noddings.
p. cm.—(Journal for research in mathematics education.
Monograph ;no. 4)
Includes bibliographical references.
ISNB 0-87353-300-3
1. Mathematics—Study and teaching. I. Davis, Robert B.
(Robert Benjamin), 1926– . II. Maher, Carolyn Alexander. III.
Noddings, Nel. IV. Series.
QA12.C654 1990
510′.71d—dc20 90-45001
CIP

The National Council of Teachers of Mathematics is a public voice of mathematics education, providing vision, leadership, and professional development to support teachers in ensuring mathematics learning of the highest quality for all students.

The publications of the National Council of Teachers of Mathematics present a variety of viewpoints. The views expressed or implied in this publication, unless otherwise noted, should not be interpreted as official positions of the Council.

Printed in the United States of America

Table of Contents

Acknowledgments

There are many who made possible the completion of this monograph and to whom we wish to express our appreciation. First, to the sponsors of the initial 1986 working conference: Martin Friedman, Director of the Office of Teacher Education, New Jersey Department of Higher Education, and Gerald A. Goldin, Director of the Rutgers University Center for Mathematics, Science and Computer Education. Their support and vision made possible the forum that initiated this work. Second, to the colleagues who presented position papers at the working conference and stimulated discussion and thought on timely issues. Third, to the graduate students who read and commented on the first draft of the manuscript; and fourth, to the many support staff who assisted in the technical preparation of the manuscript: Lynda Smith Deming for her attention to the many details in the copy editing and organization and for her illustrations in Chapters 5, 6, 7 and 11; Barbara Smith, for her typing, organizing and generally invaluable assistance.

Special thanks are expressed to the anonymous reviewers of drafts of this manuscript. Their suggestions were very helpful to us in preparing the final version.

Lastly, but most importantly, we wish to thank both the teachers with whom we work and our students. They continue to help us learn about learning and teaching.

Background: A Call to Action

This monograph grew out of a cooperative effort to improve the teaching and learning of mathematics, although in the beginning no thought was given to writing a treatise on constructivism. At the October 1985 meeting of the North American Section of the International Group for the Psychology of Mathematics Education (PME-NA) in Columbus, Ohio a group of approximately fifteen mathematics educators concerned about the current status of mathematics education met to discuss the need to address important issues regarding research on teaching and learning mathematics. At this meeting the decision was made to establish a national steering committee charged with planning a national conference to address important issues related to teaching and learning. Members of this committee were Jere Confrey (Cornell University), Gerald A. Goldin (Rutgers University), Richard Lesh (presently with Educational Testing Service, Princeton), Carolyn A. Maher, Chair and Organizer (Rutgers University), Nel Noddings (Stanford University) and Karen Schultz (Georgia State University). It was decided that this conference would be held at Rutgers University and that nationally prominent mathematics educators would be invited to participate.

The goal of the conference was to propose practical programs for reform in teaching and learning mathematics. Ten speakers, each widely regarded as an authority in mathematics education, were invited to prepare papers describing their work and ideas. These papers were distributed in advance of the conference to all participants in order to enhance the quality of the discussions. Because it was recognized that the exchanges of view among the theorists, researchers, and practitioners of mathematics education would enrich any proposals for action that might come out of the conference, it was decided that a representative audience of educators would react to and evaluate critically the proposals presented. One common theme of the papers and the discussions of them was that an individual's views about the nature of mathematical activity have direct bearing on the ways in which reform in mathematics education can be approached. Furthermore, it was generally accepted that a constructivist perspective offered the greatest promise in this regard. This monograph, then, represents the culmination of five years of collaborative discussions among individuals interested in improving the teaching and learning of mathematics.

Introduction: Constructivist Views on the Teaching and Learning of Mathematics

Robert B. Davis
Rutgers University

Carolyn A. Maher
Rutgers University

Nel Noddings
Stanford University

By now nearly everyone has probably read, or at least heard of, the recent spate of reports showing that students in the United States are not doing very well in mathematics (Dossey, Mullis, Lindquist & Chambers, 1988; McKnight et al., 1987). Although some gains in student performance have been made in recent years, most of them have been in lower-order skills. "Most students, even at age 17, do not possess the breadth and depth of mathematics proficiency needed for advanced study in secondary school mathematics" (Dossey et al., 1988, p. 10). The NAEP authors (Dossey et al.) note that only six per cent of 17-year-olds can solve multi-step problems involving simple algebra. Such results are deeply disappointing at the close of NCTM's "decade of problem solving."

This leaves the United States with what might be called a war on two fronts. There is, first, the *fact* of unsatisfactory results. But the second front is perhaps even more threatening: there is major disagreement on how to proceed in order to make things better. One school of thought would argue for "more" and "more explicit." That is to say, they would argue that the United States needs more days of school per year, or more hours of mathematics instruction per week, or more homework, or all of the above, together with a highly explicit identification of the knowledge that we want students to acquire, and a sharply directed emphasis on precisely this knowledge. Presecriptions in this direction usually suggest more frequent testing, and making more—perhaps even teachers' salaries—depend upon the outcome of this testing.

A different diagnosis and prescription might be said to tend in nearly the opposite direction (see, for example, Whitney, 1985). These recommendations argue for making mathematics more natural, fitting it better into the context of children's lives, conceivably even moving toward less testing, or at least testing with less threatening implications. The underlying rationale for this kind of change has been argued by, among others, Brown, Collins, and Duguid (1989) and Davis (1989). Solutions more consistent with this second point of view have also appeared, and have been argued very well indeed, in reports such as the NCTM's *Standards* (National Council of Teachers of Mathematics, 1989) and the National Research Council's *Everybody Counts* (National Research Council, 1989).

The level of disagreement is creating a situation in which one "reform" threatens to undo another. Some researchers pin their hopes for improvement on direct instruction and more carefully supervised practice. Others recommend greater use of small group arrangements in which students help each other, gain incentives through competition with other groups, or learn through teaching younger children.

This monograph springs from the conviction of the authors that more candid discussion of these differences is nowadays an urgent necessity. We are not alone. Indeed, there is a trend in the major national reports to suggest tackling the problem at even a deeper level, that is, one in which the questions are centered around such issues as a consideration of the nature of mathematics, what it means to think mathematically, what it means to think like a mathematician, and what it means to engage in mathematical activity. The different—one might say, "opposing"—perspectives carry important implications for what classroom teachers should do, for what evaluation should look like, and even for the selection of appropriate research methodology. If we regard doing mathematics as the following of explicit rules, then a certain kind of instruction should be employed, and a certain kind of research activity seems to be called for. If we regard the doing of mathematics as involving complex processes that call for the use of heuristics and analyses, then another kind of learning activity becomes appropriate, and another mode of inquiry is needed. The views about mathematics and the nature of mathematical thought have direct implication to research practice. The approaches are incompatible and differ substantially in their emphasis. We can expect lively debate in the next few years over these issues.

In 1985, when the present cooperative venture began to take shape, one hardly ever heard the word "constructivism." That has somehow changed. For whatever subtle reasons, the *Standards-Everybody Counts* position has, for some researchers at least, coalesced into a very active concern to spell out, and analyze, the foundations of constructivism. The word has almost become a battle cry for a reconsideration of our problems and our best road toward solution.

The title of this volume, *Constructivist Views on the Teaching and Learning of Mathematics*, suggests that we endorse an emphasis on this kind of consideration. We do. Many people other than mathematicians engage in mathematical activity, and their interests properly vary over a wide range. While engaged in mathematical activity, all of them have to hypothesize, try things out, execute mathematical procedures, communicate and defend results, and reflect on the methods selected and results generated. From a constructivist perspective these activities are all part of what it means to engage in mathematics. Learning mathematics requires construction, not passive reception, and to know mathematics requires constructive work with mathematical objects in a mathematical community. Mathematics teachers, therefore, need to accept as a major task the responsibility for establishing a mathematical environment in their classrooms.

Neither writers nor readers of this volume must pass a test of orthodoxy. As readers will discover, even those who label themselves constructivists have differences of opinion on theoretical issues and express preferences for some strategies over others. But a common thread runs through all the chapters, namely, the emphasis on mathematical activity in a mathematical community. It is assumed that learners have to construct their own knowledge—individually and collectively. Each learner has a tool kit of conceptions and skills with which he or she must construct knowledge to solve problems presented by the environment. The role of the community—other learners and teacher—is to provide the setting, pose the challenges, and offer the support that will encourage mathematical construction.

Any form of activity that takes place in a genuine community is likely to be complex. Initiates have to learn the language, customs, characteristic problems, and tools of the community, and there is a continual need to negotiate and renegotiate meaning. Because student communities necessarily lack the experience and authority of expert communities, teachers bear a great responsibility for guiding student activity, modeling mathematical behavior, and providing the examples and counterexamples that will turn student talk into useful communication about mathematics. Such responsibility requires teacher behaviors and beliefs quite different from traditional ones and, therefore, the preparation of teachers must also change. As the complexity of mathematical activity is explored, it will be clear that there are no short cuts to good teaching. There is no recipe-like method that can supplant the individual teacher working skillfully to establish a mathematical environment.

The volume begins with a consideration of the background of "constructivism." Where did this new idea come from, and what does it mean? (As with many "new ideas," it will turn out not to be all that new.) We then undertake an exploration of what it means to carry out the process of "mathematical thinking," how children characteristically engage in mathematical activity, and how teachers can promote this activity. Finally, we look at implications for teacher education, and for the ways that researchers and teachers can most effectively work together.

Throughout, readers will find an emphasis on establishing a mathematical community—providing objects that can be used in mathematical investigation, engaging in lots of teacher-student interaction for purposes of diagnosis and guidance, encouraging student-to-student talk that focuses on mathematical issues, modeling mathematical thinking, promoting the kinds of questions and comments that help community members to challenge and defend their own constructions. How do teachers best learn to conduct such complex activities? This volume is offered as a contribution to the long, hard effort to construct a satisfactory answer to such questions and, hopefully, to increase the likelihood that the United States will find appropriate ways to improve the teaching and learning of mathematics throughout the country.

PART ONE

CONSTRUCTIVISM: PROMISE AND PROBLEMS

Chapter 1: Constructivism in Mathematics Education

Nel Noddings
Stanford University

Constructivism is a popular position today not only in mathematics education (von Glasersfeld, 1987a) but in developmental psychology, theories of the family, human sexuality, psychology of gender (Hare-Mustin & Marecek, 1988), and even computer technology (Forman & Pufall, 1988). It is also the center of considerable controversy in mathematics education (Brophy, 1986a; Confrey, 1986). In a spirit of support for what constructivists are trying to accomplish, I want to discuss some strengths and weaknesses in the position. In particular, I will suggest that constructivism is not a strong epistemological position despite its adherents' claims. Indeed it might best be offered as a post-epistemological perspective.

I will begin by providing some background on constructivism; next I will discuss its epistemological weaknesses and, finally, its great strengths as a pedagogical view.

Background

Constructivism may be characterized as both a cognitive position and a methodological perspective (Noddings, 1973). As a methodological perspective in the social sciences, constructivism assumes that human beings are knowing subjects, that human behavior is mainly purposive, and that present-day human organisms have a highly developed capacity for organizing knowledge (Magoon, 1977). These assumptions suggest methods—ethnography, clinical interviews, overt thinking, and the like—specially designed to study complex semi-autonomous systems.

As a cognitive position, constructivism holds that all knowledge is constructed and that the instruments of construction include cognitive structures that are either innate (Chomsky, 1968; 1971) or are themselves products of developmental construction (Piaget, 1953; 1970a; 1971a). The latter interpretation is more characteristic of constructivism as a cognitive position, and it is the one held by most constructivists in mathematics education.

A philosophical shift in the 1960's and 70's from behaviorism to various forms of structuralism and cognitivism induced exciting changes in psychology, sociology, linguistics, and anthropology. It also revived and invigorated a whole field of study—psycholinguistics (Slobin, 1971). Cognitive psychology renewed its interest in concept formation, complex

---

I want to thank Jim Greeno and Denis Phillips for helpful suggestions on a first draft.

problem solving, and the connection between cognitive structures and behavior. One form of cognitivism became known as constructivism. Ulric Neisser describes it as follows:

> The present approach is more closely related to that of Bartlett (1932, 1958) than to any other contemporary psychologist, while its roots are at least as old as the "act psychology" of the nineteenth century. The central assertion is that seeing, hearing, and remembering are all acts of construction, which may make more or less use of stimulus information depending on circumstances. (1967, p. 10)

Here we note something that will be important in the later discussion. According to Neisser, all mental processes are constructive, and the line between perception and cognition is blurred. Even the processes often regarded as passive, such as seeing and hearing, are described as constructive. If Neisser is correct, then learners are necessarily performing acts of construction even in situations of so-called rote learning. I will return to the problems this raises for constructivist teaching when I discuss the connection between activity and learning, but for now it is enough to note that constructivists in mathematics education do not disagree with Neisser's description of cognitive activity. Von Glasersfeld (1987b), for example, says, "perceiving, from a constructivist point of view, is always an active making rather than a passive receiving . . ." (p. 217).

While Neisser traced his constructivism to *act psychology*, Piaget traced his more directly to Kantian philosophy. In *Insights and Illusions of Philosophy* (1971b), he credited Kant with the first description of an epistemological subject. Kant, that is, described the structures by which any competent subject acquires or generates knowledge. Piaget followed Kant in distinguishing between empirical knowledge (knowledge of the contingent world) and logico-mathematical knowledge (knowledge of necessary truths). But he broke with Kant in describing cognitive structures as products of development rather than innate structures. This is a matter on which he also differed from Chomsky. Whereas Chomsky holds that the linguistic structures of mind are innate, Piaget insisted that certain logical structures, developed through the coordination of actions, precede linguistic development and make the construction of linguistic structures possible (1971a). Although both Chomsky and Piaget call for the development of competence theories that describe the structures of mind (Noddings, 1974), Chomsky's view is anchored in the philosophical tradition of rationalism, while Piaget's is much closer to the dynamic perspective of pragmatism.

In accepting the Kantian distinction between empirical and logico-mathematical knowledge, Piaget accepted the difficult task of explaining the development of cognitive mathematical structures. Here Piaget relied on the concept of reflective abstraction. Reflective abstraction is different from classical abstraction in that it does not proceed from a series of observations of contingent events or objects. Rather, it is a process of interiorizing our physical operations on objects. As we move sets of objects about (put them together, rearrange them, separate them), we interiorize properties of mathematical operations rather than objects; we acquire implicit understanding of commutativity, associativity, and reversibility. Here the claim is that there is an essential connection between purposive activity and the development of cognitive structure. There is also a recognition (sometimes overlooked by contemporary radical constructivists) that the objects play a role in reflective abstraction; that is, epistemological subjects and objects are indissociably linked in operational events. We cannot force certain results onto the objects we operate on. Our operations are somehow constrained. There is an inevitability about the outcomes and characteristics of operations. That is why the resulting structures are logico-mathematical and why their workings are marked by necessity. This conclusion suggests a challenge to those constructivists who emphasize the uniqueness of individual constructions, and I will discuss the problems of conflating individual subject and epistemological subject a bit later.

Piaget's theories are, in the important sense just described, thoroughly constructivist. Not only are intellectual processes themselves constructive—a point on which both Neisser and Chomsky would agree—but cognitive structures themselves are products of continued construction. Constructivism is rooted in the idea of an epistemological subject, an active knowing mechanism that knows through continued construction. This active construction implies both a base structure from which to begin construction (a structure of assimilation) and a process of transformation or creation which is the construction. It implies, also, a process of continual revision of structure (a process of accommodation). Finally, Piaget's cognitive constructivism leads logically to methodological constructivism. The need to identify and describe various cognitive structures in all phases of construction suggests methods such as the clinical interview and prolonged observation that permit us to make inferences about the structures that underlie behavior.

So far I have concentrated on constructivist writings and debates two decades old. A search of current literature shows that the concept pops up everywhere. For example, Thoresen (1988) has raised questions about the rigor and clarity of "constructivism" in counseling psychology. But, although mathematics educators also cite some recent thinkers on constructivism (see other chapters in this volume), there seem to be few epistemological advances beyond Piaget. This is not to say that there have been no advances in the psychological aspects of constructivism. Cognitive scientists and mathematics educators who favor the cognitive science approach have moved well beyond Piaget in describing the way "minds" operate to build representations, retrieve "frames," copy items from long term memory, and match initial frames with the demands of a current problem. (See, for example, Davis, 1984; Kintsch & Greeno, 1985; Papert, 1980; Simon, 1979). However, most of these researchers are interested in the way our minds work, not in the epistemological status of the mind's products. Further, their language—"copying," "non-destructive read outs," "frames," "retrieval"—is highly colored by work with computers. There is a shift from the organic language of Piaget to machine language. Many such writers do not even use the word constructivism, although they embrace the central idea that the operations of mind are constructed. I intend no criticism in these remarks about cognitive science advances, but I want to emphasize the psychological and pedagogical aspects of these advances; they are not epistemological.

Constructivists in mathematics education contend that cognitive constructivism implies pedagogical constructivism; that is, acceptance of constructivist premises about knowledge and knowers implies a way of teaching that acknowledges learners as active knowers. As Gerald Goldin notes in his chapter in this volume, it is clear that one can embrace the pedagogical methods suggested by constructivists without accepting constructivist premises. It may also be the case that a convinced philosophical constructivist need not, logically, employ only so-called constructivist methods. That will be an important issue when we discuss the connection between activity and learning.

Although there are conceptual differences in current constructivist views (and some of these will be important in the coming analysis), constructivists generally agree on the following:

1. All knowledge is constructed. Mathematical knowledge is constructed, at least in part, through a process of reflective abstraction.
2. There exist cognitive structures that are activated in the processes of construction. These structures account for the construction; that is, they explain the result of cognitive activity in roughly the way a computer program accounts for the output of a computer.
3. Cognitive structures are under continual development. Purposive activity induces transformation of existing structures. The environment presses the organism to adapt.
4. Acknowledgment of constructivism as a cognitive position leads to the adoption of methodological constructivism.
    a. Methodological constructivism in research develops methods of study consonant with the assumption of cognitive constructivism.
    b. Pedagogical constructivism suggests methods of teaching consonant with cognitive constructivism.

Constructivism as Epistemology

All knowledge is constructed (von Glasersfeld, 1987a). Is this an epistemological or a psychological claim? Constructivists, following Piaget, usually reject this question as a form of philosophical error. In this view epistemology and psychology are so intricately bound up in each other that it makes no sense to try to separate them. Constructivists have an important insight here—one shared in part by earlier pragmatists and contemporary philosophers whose views of knowledge tend toward pragmatism. Wittgenstein, even in his positivist days, dismissed epistemology as "the philosophy of psychology" (1961), and more recently W. V. O. Quine has argued for the "naturalization of epistemology" (1969). Richard Rorty (1979) goes even further and suggests that both traditional epistemology and the various structuralisms of Piaget, Chomsky, Levi-Strauss, Marx, and Freud are on a similar wrong track (p. 249)—the quest for a description of nature through the workings of mind.

I think Rorty is right when he says that the attempt to construct or discover a foundation for science (and all knowledge) is hopeless whether one depends on the structures of perception (observation), self-evident truths, or cognition. But even if foundational epistemology is rejected (and this is what constructivists should do), some epistemological questions remain, and, of course, constructivists have not rejected epistemology. Thus our initial question retains its point: What sort of assumption (epistemological, psychological, or both) is being made when one says, "All knowledge is constructed"?

The question can be logically broken into two parts. First, what has the assumption to do with judging the status of general knowledge claims? Given a statement offered as a bit of knowledge, how does the claim about construction help us to decide what becomes part of the bona fide body of knowledge and what does not? Second, if we focus on knowers, how do we judge when they know and when they do not? These are two basic questions of epistemology.

Let's consider, first, knowledge as a set of statements in the public domain. Here we are not asking what it means to say: Joe knows *p*. We are asking, rather, what it means to claim *p* as a bit of knowledge. One of the first questions we ask when we are faced with an alleged knowledge claim is, "Who said that?" If *p* is a mathematical statement, we are more likely to accept it if George Polya or John von Neumann is its source than if, say, Ronald Reagan or a local high school student came up with it. The mathematicians have an authority that the other two do not have.

But our judgment is not based on raw authority. The mathematicians' authority is not like that of the pope (or, at least, it shouldn't be). We do not accept their word simply because their office confers unassailable authority. Rather we accept *p*, tentatively, because we know that mathematicians belong to a community that subjects all knowledge claims to careful scrutiny, and the criteria for such scrutiny are laid out for all the community to see.

The fact (if it is one) that *p* was constructed is irrelevant as a criterion for its status as knowledge. Constructivists are right when they suggest that the genesis of *p* is not irrelevant to the growth of mathematical knowledge, nor is it irrelevant to someone's learning about *p* . Studying the construction of *p* can lead to a host of objections, revisions, and new hypotheses (Lakatos, 1976), and it can provide insight for learners. What the construction cannot do, however, unless it is part of the proof itself, is to establish *p*'s status as knowledge.

The fact that *p* was constructed tells us nothing about truth, knowledge, the justification of belief, or the nature of evidence—all traditional interests in epistemology. Rather, the constructivist assumption should be followed by a break with epistemology. Having accepted the basic constructivist premise, there is no point in looking for foundations or using the language of absolute truth. The constructivist position is really post-epistemological, and that is why it can be so powerful in inducing new methods of research and teaching. It recognizes the power of the environment to press for adaptation, the temporality of knowledge, and the existence of multiple selves behaving in consonance with the rules of various subcultures. What is left of epistemological questions may be divided among mathematics (its canons and methods), the sociology of knowledge (what groups have the power to label *p* knowledge), and the psychology of learning and teaching.

Many of the traditional questions of epistemology would be shifted to mathematics itself. Here, clearly, a body of knowledge is continually under construction, and some nucleus of it is firmly established. Mathematicians need not answer the question what knowledge is generally; they need only describe mathematical knowledge and the tests a proposition must pass to be admitted to that body of knowledge. In an important sense, at any given time, there is a world of mathematics already established to be discovered by individual students. If a student picks up a bit of this pre-established material, does he or she have knowledge? Under what circumstances?

These questions lead us to the second part of our question: How does the constructivist assumption help us to decide whether a knower knows? All knowledge is constructed. If Neisser's premise—that all mental acts are constructive—is accepted, then this basic claim—as an epistemological claim—is trivial. We cannot distinguish between knowledge and other mental products, or even errors, by virtue of their construction. A difficulty that arises in constructivist talk is this: On the one hand, if students memorize *p*, we often deny that the students have knowledge of *p*, even if *p* is well established in the public domain; if, on the other hand, students come up with *q* as a result of construction, we sometimes accept *q* as knowledge even if it is demonstrably false.

Consider, first, constructions that are somehow faulty or lead to results that are wrong. The most notorious is Erlwanger's Benny (1973). Benny had a system for converting his answers to the ones on the answer sheet provided by the curriculum. His method was systematic, and he could explain it. Converting 3/2 to .5, for example, involved adding 2 and 3 and prefixing a decimal point. That this rule also made it possible to convert 2/3 to .5 did not seem to bother Benny.

Constructivists often point to the case of Benny because it illustrates how badly mathematics can be learned when a curriculum does not encourage mathematical thinking. But the problem here is not that Benny fails to construct (he could hardly avoid doing so) but, rather, that the environment fails to press Benny to correct his misconceptions. The constructivist teacher would prefer to help Benny by having him explore whether the result 3/2 = 2/3 is satisfactory. If it is not, then some change in his procedural rules is clearly necessary. But old-fashioned behaviorists might simply put Benny on a schedule of practice that includes very careful evaluation of his responses and immediate feedback. Benny, by definition, would still be constructing, but constructivists consider constructions performed in such situations to be less powerful than the sort generated by personal puzzlement, goal-setting, testing hypotheses, etc.

In rejecting Benny's claims to knowledge, constructivists should abandon traditional epistemological talk. Here is a construction. In a domain other than mathematics—with some other, nonmathematical, objects—this construction of Benny's might make sense. Indeed Benny's response to the curriculum that isolated him so completely was an adaptive response. He succeeded at whatever game he was playing, but he was not playing the game of mathematics. This suggests—and here is the great strength of pedagogical constructivism—that the teacher's main function is to establish a mathematical environment.

A second, obverse, difficulty arises when constructivists want to deny that rote responses represent knowledge. If a student recites a bit of arithmetical information, for example, but does not understand where this information came from or how it can be used, we often say the student does not "really know." We reject his statement as a knowledge claim.

Now, traditional epistemology can do this because it has a criterion of justified true belief that must be applied to every case of claiming to know. This assumes that things can be true quite independently of any knower's activity. For A to know x x must be true, A must believe x and A must have good reasons for believing x. The student who simply parrots something may indeed be denied a claim to knowledge. (Even this is not a simple matter, however, because we can find substantial philosophical reasons for accepting "the teacher said so" as a good enough reason to support a student's claim! For more on "epistemic dependence," see Siegel, 1988.) To reject as knowledge a claim that the community accepts as true is a tricky business.

How can constructivists reject such a knowledge claim? They might begin by saying that the student cannot give an adequate account of *x*. For example, how is *x* derived? But we do not expect students to be able to give this sort of account of most *x* 's. "How did you get it?" is the question we usually ask. The answers we accept to this question are based inevitably on the already established body of mathematical knowledge and the canons of thinking laid down by the mathematical community.

The constructivist suggests that we can make a decision on the basis of whether or not *x* was constructed. But does this make sense? As a cognitive position, constructivism asserts that all mental activity is constructive. Even when students are in what look to be rote learning situations, they must perforce construct, because that is the way the mind operates. So it seems to me that constructivists should talk about weak and strong acts of construction rather than acts involving or not involving construction. In mathematical environments, strong acts of construction would no doubt be those recognized by mathematicians as mathematical; weak constructions would be those evaluated as limited in mathematical use. (I have already discussed those—like Benny's—that might be judged faulty because they do not belong at all to the applicable mathematical domain.)

Some genuine and very tough questions about teaching follow. Might it not be the case, for example, that some students perform strong acts of construction no matter how the material is presented? And might it not also be the case that, while the teacher is encouraging exploration and genuine (strong) acts of construction, some students perform weak acts such as quietly waiting for group consensus and then noting the answer?

Both aspects of the question about a knower's status need further analysis, elaboration, and clarification. It is by no means clear that the current use of epistemological language will be particularly helpful in this task. What is clear is that the emphasis on construction forces us to probe deeply into students' activity. How firm a grasp do they have on the material? What can they do with it? What misconceptions do they entertain? Even if they are producing wrong answers, are they constructing in a way that is mathematically recognizable? These are among the questions we need to ask in order to teach effectively, and they are not epistemological.

Methodological Constructivism

Acceptance of the premise that knowledge and (many constructivists would say) reality itself are constructed leads to methodological constructivism. In research this means that we have to investigate our subjects' perceptions, purposes, premises, and ways of working things out if we are to understand their behavior. Even at the contextual level, as we try to understand the effects of physical and cultural environments on people, we have to look at their purposive interaction with those environments. We no longer believe that people are simply caused to behave in certain ways by an environment that is entirely external to and independent of their cognitive processes.

For teachers, methodological constructivism becomes pedagogical constructivism. In order to teach well, we need to know what our students are thinking, how they produce the chain of little marks we see on their papers, and what they can do (or want to do) with the material we present to them. But the cognitive premises of constructivism can dictate only guidelines for good teaching. We cannot derive from them, any more than we can from any other cognitive position, specific teaching methods.

Pedagogical constructivism suggests more sophisticated diagnostic tools—tools that will uncover patterns of thinking, systematic errors, persistent misconceptions (see Confrey, this volume). Further, the elaboration required in, say, thinking aloud in the presence of a teacher encourages students to concentrate on the question or problem at hand. Conducted well, such a session gives the teacher many opportunities to reassure students that they are doing some things right, that their thinking has some power, that their errors are correctable. Above all such a method can be used to create a mathematical environment—one that will press for mathematical adaptation rather than a form suitable for another environment.

Overt thinking is, or can be, a powerful teaching method as well as a diagnostic tool, but teachers need not be confined to it by their constructivism. For example, if a teacher learns through such a diagnostic session that Betsy is making a certain kind of error over and over, it seems perfectly reasonable to show her how to do the procedure correctly and give her a batch of practice exercises. It may indeed be reasonable to provide whole classes with drill and practice at appropriate times. In particular if it is clear that performance errors (e.g., wrongly combining or simplifying radicals) are getting in the way of concentrating on more significant problems, straightforward practice may actually facilitate genuine problem solving.

I am not recommending that students be kept at drill and practice for days or years on end (until, as some say, they've mastered the basics). Rather, I'm suggesting that teachers anticipate some of the skills that students will likely need to construct important concepts and principles. Students need building materials, tools, patterns, and sound work habits if they are to construct mathematical objects and relationships. Some of these materials, tools, and patterns can and should be created through strong acts of construction by the students themselves; others might simply be accepted and tried out on trust (weak acts, but not faulty).

Constructivist premises imply that there will be many roads to most solutions or instructional endpoints. We cannot, therefore, be sure that all students will find the anticipated skills necessary or even useful in their constructions. But there is a high probability that some particular skills will be needed in any given task. Any teacher who has conducted an overt thinking session sympathizes with students who must agonize over every step of a solution—often forgetting in the process why they are dividing, or solving a proportion, or factoring an unwieldy expression. My point here is that we need not discard all of the strategies recommended by theorists who espouse direct instruction (Brophy, 1986a; Good, Grouws, & Ebmeier, 1983) even if we disagree with them on fundamental cognitive premises (Noddings, 1986).

Many mathematics educators recognize the power of "constructivist methods" in one-to-one situations, but they also see that schoolteachers cannot work continuously in such situations (Cobb, Wood, & Yackel, this volume). Classroom conditions force us to think about instructional economies. Constructivist teachers have to keep their basic premises in mind, but they should feel free to adapt a wide variety of methods for their own purposes. Given our premises, we need to get thinking out into the open, to encourage students to conceive their own mathematical purposes and execute their own plans, and to provide situations and objects that may trigger conflict (disequilibrium) and reflective abstraction. How can we do all this with a classroom full of students, and what pitfalls lie in our way?

Consider, first, the common constructivist recommendation that teachers make heavy use of manipulatives. This recommendation was an early and plausible attempt to apply Piagetian theory directly to teaching. If reflective abstraction proceeds from the operations we perform on objects, then it makes sense to have our students work with objects. The difficulty, of course, is that students must have a purpose for engaging in the manipulation of objects. Otherwise, objects can be as mysterious as numerals; even Cuisenaire rods can become "symbols made of colored wood" (Holt, 1964).

Understanding this possibility, we need, perhaps, to provide some direct instruction on the use of various manipulatives and then simply make them available. In actual problem solving situations, we probably should not guide students in their use. If we do, we are likely to detach students from their own purposes and set them blindly to work on our own. Caveats of this sort spring up everywhere in constructivist teaching. Students will construct, but we want their constructions to be guided by mathematical purposes, not by the need to figure out what teachers want or where they are headed.

Next, because teachers have to work with many children, it makes sense to ask whether there is a way to approximate the one-to-one situation with a whole class. Can we elicit genuine student thinking in the whole class situation? Several promising models have appeared (see the essays in this volume and also Davis, 1984; Lampert, 1988; Schoenfeld, 1985; Steffe, Cobb, & von Glasersfeld, 1988). All of these methods share a common characteristic: They are all highly interactive. Teachers both model and elicit, but they model by asking questions, following leads, and conjecturing rather than presenting faultless products. Teaching this way requires considerable mathematical knowledge as well as pedagogical skill. How can teachers follow students' suggestions if they do not know enough mathematics to perceive where the suggestions may lead? This is a problem for teacher education.

But a caveat again arises directly out of the constructivist framework. While a lesson of the sort advocated above is conducted, students will be "constructing." Some will be performing strong (mathematical) acts of construction. Hearing evidence of such thinking, teachers (and observers) may be delighted with the lesson. But other students (how many?) may be performing weak acts on the problem at hand, and some may be "chasing deer in the wildwood" as Virgil Mallory used to say. It would, therefore, seem unwise to rely on such lessons day in and day out.

How else can we induce the engagement that is essential if students are to perform powerful constructions? One possibility is to increase the amount of time students spend working together (see Cobb, Wood, & Yackel; Maher & Alston, this volume). The use of small groups in cooperative learning is becoming a popular strategy, and there are sound cognitive reasons for allowing students to work together. Vygotsky (1978) posited group interaction as one source in the development of mental operations; that is, he suggested that children gradually internalize the talk that occurs in groups. They begin to challenge themselves, ask for reasons, and in general monitor their own mental work as others do their public speech. Cobb, Wood, and Yackel follow a line of thinking called "social constructivism" that puts great emphasis on the processes of communicating and negotiating in communities. A difficulty here is that, once again, we must somehow ensure that the community is a mathematical community. To assume that the deliberations of any community—conducted by some general plan of right action—will lead to acceptable mathematical results suggests a traditional epistemology. In a post-epistemological perspective, we recognize the canons and ways authorized by this particular community. (On the possibility of construing epistemology as itself the study of human understanding, see Toulmin, 1972.)

But group work is not a pedagogical panacea in any case (see Noddings, 1989). Some students may participate eagerly while others sit out the session waiting for answers to develop. Assigning rigid roles so that everyone has to participate can distract students' attention from mathematics to the group process itself. Further, students can be rude and cruel to one another, and teachers have to watch group operations to be sure that students are learning to help and care for each other—not just to solve problems in expeditious ways.

Here, too, there is a large part for teacher education to play. The literature on small groups and cooperative learning is growing rapidly. What kind of small group scheme should teachers use? How should groups be constituted? For what kinds of task? Should there be inter-group competition? Should teachers use individual or group evaluation? Will the end-product be a group one or set of individual ones (Noddings, 1989)? Teachers need to be well-informed in order to use these methods effectively. Further, constructivist teachers need practice in selecting and justifying the forms that are compatible with constructivist premises.

The great strength of constructivism is that it leads us to think critically and imaginatively about the teaching-learning process. Believing the premises of constructivism, we no longer look for simple solutions, and we have a powerful set of criteria by which to judge our possible choices of teaching method.

I will close by giving a simple example of a teacher's constructivist thinking. Suppose I am concentrating on the central problem of getting my students' thinking out into the open. As I mark a set of tests, I realize that, alas, students are not showing their work as I have instructed them to do. Then I look at what I'm doing—taking off points here and there for small or large errors. Aha! Suppose I switch to a positive scheme of grading? The next day, and before every written exercise thereafter, I remind students that I'll be searching for thoughts to reward. They will get points for useful pictures, charts, formulas, statements that suggest either hypotheses or doubts, challenges to the question itself. And then I do this. No more -2s and -10s. Their papers will, rather, be peppered with +2s and +10s together with remarks encouraging attempts or explaining why an attempt failed. The result should be lots more student talk on paper. (It worked for me, by the way.) This is just one example of constructivist thinking applied to an everyday problem of schoolteaching, but it illustrates the power of constructivism as a cognitive and methodological position.

Conclusion

Constructivism is, logically, a post-epistemological position. The standard questions of epistemology cannot be answered—or even reasonably asked—from this perspective. Its premises suggest, rather, abandonment of traditional epistemological language. This move leads us to concentrate on constructivism as a cognitive position and methodological perspective. As such, it can be powerful in helping us to study mathematical learning, to develop appropriate teaching strategies, and to reflect on the everyday problems of schoolteaching. But it requires considerably more analysis and elaboration in the community of mathematics educators if it is to meet the kinds of legitimate objections I have noted here.

Chapter 2: An Exposition of Constructivism: Why Some Like It Radical

Ernst von Glasersfeld
Scientific Reasoning Research Institute
University of Massachusetts

> Man, having within himself an imagined world of lines and numbers, operates in it with abstractions just as God, in the universe, did with reality.
>
> Giambattista Vico[1]

When the Neapolitan philosopher Giambattista Vico published his treatise on the construction of knowledge,[2] it triggered quite a controversy in the *Giornale de'Letterati d'Italia*, one of the most prestigious scholarly journals at the time. This was in the years 1710-12. The first reviewer, who remained anonymous, had carefully read the treatise and was obviously shocked by the implications it had for traditional epistemology—all the more so because, as he conceded, the arguments showed great learning and were presented with elegance. He was therefore impelled to question Vico's position, and he very politely suggested that one thing was lacking in the treatise: the proof that what it asserted was true.[3]

Today, those constructivists who are "radical" because they take their theory of knowing seriously frequently meet the same objection—except that it is sometimes expressed less politely than at the beginning of the 18th century. Now, no less than then, it is difficult to show the critics that what they demand is the very thing constructivism must do without. To claim that one's theory of knowing is true, in the traditional sense of representing a state or feature of an experiencer-independent world, would be perjury for a radical constructivist. One of the central points of the theory is precisely that this kind of "truth" can never be claimed for the knowledge (or any piece of it) that human reason produces.

To mark this radical departure, I have in the last few years taken to calling my orientation a theory of knowing rather than a "theory of knowledge." I agree whole-heartedly with Noddings when she says, at the beginning of her contribution to this volume, that radical constructivism should be "offered as a post-epistemological perspective." One of the consequences of such an appraisal, however, must be that one does not persist in arguing against it as though it were or purported to be a traditional theory of knowledge. Another consequence—for me the more important one—is that constructivism needs to be radical and must explain that one can, indeed, manage without the traditional notion of Truth. That this task is possible may become more plausible if I trace the sources of some of the ideas that made the enterprise seem desirable. In retrospect, the path along which I picked up relevant ideas (somewhat abbreviated and idealized) led from the early doubts of the Pre-Socratics, via Montaigne, Berkeley, Vico, and Kant, to thinkers who developed instrumentalism and pragmatism at the turn of this century, and eventually to the Italian Operational School and Piaget's genetic epistemology.

The Way of the Sceptics

To Xenophanes (6th century B.C.) we may credit the insight that even if someone succeeded in describing exactly how the world really is, he or she would have no way of knowing that it was the "true" description.[4] This is the major argument the sceptics have repeated for two thousand five hundred years. It is based on the assumption that whatever ideas or knowledge we have must have been derived in some way from our experience, which includes sensing, acting, and thinking. If this is the case, we have no way of checking the truth of our knowledge with the world presumed to be lying beyond our experiential interface, because to do this, we would need an access to such a world that does not involve our experiencing it. Plato tried to get around this by claiming that some god had placed the pure ideas inside us and that experience with the fuzzy, imperfect world of the senses could only serve to make us "remember" what was really true. Thus, there would be no need (and no way) to check our knowledge against an independent external reality. Consequently, in Plato's famous metaphor, the man who is led out of the cave of his commonplace experience is blinded by a splendid vision. But his vision is the pure realm of an interpersonal soul and not the fuzzy world perceived by the senses.[5] From my point of view, Plato created an ingenious poetic or "metaphysical" myth, but not a rational theory of knowing. The sceptic's position, developed into a school under Pyrrho at the end of the next century, was diligently compiled and documented by Sextus Empiricus about 200 A.D. It smoldered under the theological debates of the middle ages and burst into full flame in the 16th century when the works of Sextus Empiricus were rediscovered. Descartes set out to put an end to it, but succeeded only in strengthening the side he was opposing (cf. Popkin, 1979). The British Empiricists then helped to harden the skeptical doctrine by their detailed analyses. First, Locke discarded the secondary (sensory) properties of things as sources of "true" information about the real world. Then, Berkeley showed that Locke's arguments applied equally to the primary properties (spatial extension, motion, number, etc.), and finally Hume delivered an even more serious blow by attributing the notion of causality (and other relations that serve to organize experience) to the conceptual habits of the human knower. The final demolition of realism was brought about when Kant suggested that the concepts of space and time were the necessary forms of human experience, rather than characteristics of the universe. This meant that we cannot even imagine what the structure of the real world might be like, because whatever we call structure is necessarily an arrangement in space, time, or both.

These are extremely uncomfortable arguments. Philosophers have forever tried to dismantle them, but they have had little success. The arguments are uncomfortable because they threaten a concept which we feel we cannot do without. "Knowledge" is something of which we are quite sure that we have a certain amount, and we are not prepared to relinquish it.

The trouble is that throughout the occidental history of ideas and right down to our own days, two requisites have been considered fundamental in any epistemological discussion of knowledge. The first of these requisites demands that whatever we would like to call "true knowledge" has to be independent of the knowing subject. The second requisite is that knowledge is to be taken seriously only if it claims to represent a world of "things-in-themselves" in a more or less veridical fashion. In other words, it is tacitly taken for granted that a fully structured and knowable world "exists" and that it is the business of the cognizing human subject to discover what that structure is.

The weakness of the sceptics' position lies in its polemical formulation. It always sounds as though the traditional epistemologists' definition of knowledge were the only possible one. Hence, when Montaigne says *"la peste de l'homme c'est l'opinion de savoir"* (mankind's plague is the conceit of knowing)[6], it sounds as though we ought to give up all knowing. But he was referring to absolutistic claims of experiential knowledge and was discussing them in the context of the traditional dogmatic belief that religious revelation is unquestionable. He had in mind absolute truth, and he was castigating those who claimed that a rational interpretation of experience (of which "scientific observation" is, after all, a sophisticated form) would lead to such truth. He certainly did not intend to discredit the kind of know-how that enabled his peasants to make a good wine. In short, what the sceptics failed to stress was that, though no truths about a "real" world could be derived from experience, experience nevertheless supplied a great deal of useful knowledge.

The Changed Concept of Knowledge

Unbeknownst to Kant, who in the 1780's hammered this limitation in with his Critiques of pure and practical reason, Giambattista Vico had come to a very similar conclusion in 1710. "The human mind can know only what the human mind has made" was his slogan and, more like Piaget than Kant, he did not assume that space and time were necessarily a priori categories, but suggested that they, too, were human constructs (Vico, 1858). Pursuing this way of thinking, one is led to what I have called "a reconstruction of the concept of knowledge" (von Glasersfeld, 1985). Some reconstruction is needed because, on the one hand, one can no longer maintain that the cognizing activity should or could produce a true representation of an objective world, and on the other, one does not want to end up with a solipsistic form of idealism. The only way out, then, would seem to be a drastic modification of the relation between the cognitive structures we build up and that "real" world which we are inclined to assume as "existing" beyond our perceptual interface.[7] Instead of the illusory relation of "representation," one has to find a way of relating knowledge to reality that does not imply anything like match or correspondence.

Neither Vico nor Kant explicitly mentioned such a conceptual alternative. It was supplied, however, in Darwin's theory of evolution by the concept of fit. Once this relational concept has been stripped of its erroneous formulation in the slogan "survival of the fittest" (cf. Pittendrigh, 1958; von Glasersfeld, 1980), it offers a way around the paradox of the traditional theory of knowledge. As far as I know, this was first suggested by William James (1880).[8] Georg Simmel (1885) elaborated it, and Aleksandr Bogdanov (1909) developed it into a comprehensive instrumentalist epistemology. Hans Vaihinger (1913), who had been working at his "Philosophy of As If" since the 1870's and who probably was quite unaware of Vico, re-introduced the idea of conceptual construction.

Piaget's Contribution

Today, in retrospect, these and other authors can be cited as "sources" of constructivism. However, the great pioneer of the constructivist theory of knowing, Jean Piaget, started from Kant and arrived at his view of cognition as a biologist who looked at intelligence and knowledge as biological functions whose development had to be explained and mapped in the ontogeny of organisms.

In interpreting Piaget, it is important to remember that his publications range over an astounding variety of topics and are spread over more than half a century.[9] As with any versatile and original thinker, his ideas did not cease to develop and change (Vuyk, 1981). It is, therefore, not surprising that one can spot contradictions in his work. An obvious instance is his theory of stages, which was gradually superseded by his theory of equilibration (cf. Rowell, 1989). Thus it is not too difficult to dismiss Piaget on the strength of one or two quotations or, what is even more frequent, on the strength of what superficial summarizers have said about him. It is also likely that arguments about what Piaget actually believed will continue and that different scholars will provide different interpretations. In my view, the following basic principles of radical constructivism emerge quite clearly if one tries to comprise as much as possible of Piaget's writings in one coherent theory—but I would argue for these principles even if they could be shown to diverge from Piaget's thinking.

1. Knowledge is not passively received either through the senses or by way of communication. Knowledge is actively built up by the cognizing subject.

2. a. The function of cognition is adaptive, in the biological sense of the term, tending towards fit or viability;

   b. Cognition serves the subject's organization of the experiential world, not the discovery of an objective ontological reality.

One cannot adopt these principles casually. If taken seriously, they are incompatible with the traditional notions of knowledge, truth, and objectivity, and they require a radical reconstruction of one's concept of reality. Instead of an inaccessible realm beyond perception and cognition, it now becomes the experiential world we actually live in. This world is not an unchanging independent structure, but the result of distinctions that generate a physical and a social environment to which, in turn, we adapt as best we can.

Consequently, one cannot adopt the constructivist principles as an absolute truth, but only as a working hypothesis that may or may not turn out to be viable. This is the main reason why the constructivist orientation is unequivocally post-epistemological (Noddings, this volume).

The Concept of Viability

To relinquish the inveterate belief that knowledge must eventually represent something that lies beyond our experience is, indeed, a frightening step to take. It constitutes a feat of decentering that is even more demanding than the one accomplished by a few outstanding thinkers in the 16th century who realized that the earth was not the center of the universe. Because it goes against an age-old habit, it is immensely difficult to accept that, no matter how well we can predict the results of certain actions we take or the "effects" of certain "causes" we observe, this must never be interpreted as a proof that we have discovered how the "real" world works.[10]

The key to this insight lies in what Piaget formulated in the phrase *"l'object se laisse faire"* ("the object allows itself to be treated"; 1970b, p. 35). At the symposium on the occasion of his 80th birthday he repeated the phrase and explained it further: "When one comes to have a true theory, this is because the object permitted it; which amounts to saying that it contained something analogous to my actions" (Inhelder, Garcia, & Voneche, 1977, p. 64). In this context—as in so many in Piaget's works—it is important to remember that an "object" is never a thing-in-itself for Piaget, but something that the cognizing subject has constructed by making distinctions and coordinations in his or her perceptual field (Piaget, 1937).

That is all very well, one might say, but how does it come about that the reality we construct is in many ways remarkably stable? And, one might also ask why, if we ourselves construct our experiential reality, can we not construct any reality we might like?

The first question was answered in a categorical way by George Kelly: "To the living creature, then, the universe is real, but it is not inexorable unless he chooses to construe it that way" (1955, p. 8). The living creature, be it fish, fowl, or human, thrives by abstracting regularities and rules from experience that enable it to avoid disagreeable situations and, to some extent, to generate agreeable ones. This "abstracting of regularities" is always the result of assimilation. No experience is ever the same as another in the absolute sense. Repetition and, consequently, regularity can be obtained only by disregarding certain differences. This notion of assimilation is at the core of Piaget's scheme theory. No schemes could be developed if the organism could not isolate situations in which a certain action leads to a desirable result. It is the focus on the result that distinguishes a scheme from a reflex and makes possible the form of learning that Piaget called accommodation. It takes place when a scheme does not lead to the expected result.

This produces a perturbation, and the perturbation may lead either to a modification of the pattern that was abstracted as the "triggering situation" or to a modification of the action. All this, I want to emphasize, concerns the experiential world of the acting organism, not any "external" reality. And the patterns a cognizing organism can and does abstract from experience depend on the operations of distinction and coordination the organism can and does carry out.[11] This was brilliantly demonstrated for a variety of organisms more than fifty years ago by Jakob von Uexküll (1933/1970).

The second question—why we cannot construct any reality we like—can be raised only if the concept of viability is misunderstood or ignored. The absurdity of solipsism stems from the denial of any relation between knowledge and an experiencer-independent world. Radical constructivism has been careful to stress that all action, be it physical or conceptual, is subject to constraints. I can no more walk through the desk in front of me than I can argue that black is white at one and the same time. What constrains me, however, is not quite the same in the two cases. That the desk constitutes an obstacle to my physical movement is due to the particular distinctions my sensory system enables me to make and to the particular way in which I have come to coordinate them. Indeed, if I now could walk through the desk, it would no longer fit the abstraction I have made in prior experience. This, I think, is simple enough. What is not so simple is the realization that the fact that I am able to make the particular distinctions and coordinations and establish their permanence in my experiential world does not tell me anything other than the fact that it is one of the things my experiential reality allows me to do. Using a spatial metaphor, I have at times expressed this by saying that the viability of an action shows no more than that the "real" world leaves us room to act in that way. Conversely, when my actions fail and I am compelled to make a physical or conceptual accommodation, this does not warrant the assumption that my failure reveals something that "exists" beyond my experience. Whatever obstacle I might conjecture, can be described only in terms of my own actions. (In this context, it is important to remember that the constructivist theory holds that perception is not passive, but under all circumstances the result of action [cf. Piaget, 1969].)

The constraints that preclude my saying that black is white are, of course, not physical but conceptual. The way we use symbols to handle abstractions we have made from experience requires, among other things, that we exclude contradiction (cf. von Glasersfeld, in press). Consistency, in maintaining semantic links and in avoiding contradictions, is an indispensable condition of what I would call our "rational game."

The Question of Certainty

The domain of mathematics is in some sense the epitome of the rational game. The certainty of mathematical results has often been brought up as an argument against constructivism. To indicate that the theoretical infallibility of mathematical operations (in practice, mistakes may, of course, occur) cannot be claimed as proof that these operations give access to an ontological reality, I have compared this generation of certainty to the game of chess. At the painful moment when you discover that your opponent can put you into a "checkmate" position, you have no way of doubting it and your shock is as real as any shock can be. Yet, it is obvious that the certainty you are experiencing springs from nothing but the conceptual relations that constitute the rules of the game; and it is equally obvious that these conceptual relations are absolute in the sense that if I broke them and thus destroyed the certainty they generate, I would no longer be playing that particular game.

The comparison with chess has caused remonstrations, and I would like to clarify my position. I still believe that the certainty in mathematics springs from the same conceptual source, but this does not mean that I hold mathematics to be like chess in other ways. The biggest difference is that the elements to which the rules of chess apply are all specific to the game. Flesh and blood kings cannot be put into "mate" positions, equestrian knights move unlike their chess namesakes, and living queens show their power in ways that are inconceivable on the chess board. In contrast, the elements to which the rules of mathematics are applied are not free inventions. In counting, for example, the elements start out as ordinary things that have been abstracted from ordinary experience, and the basic abstract concepts, such as "oneness" and "plurality," have a life of their own before they are incorporated into the realm of mathematics. It is precisely this connection with everyday experience and conceptual practice that leads to the contention that mathematics "reflects" the real world.

The "imagined world of lines and numbers" of which Vico speaks in the quotation I have put at the beginning of this essay is in no sense an arbitrary world. At the roots of the vast network of mathematical abstractions are the simple operations that allow us to perceive discrete items in the field of our experience, and simple relational concepts that allow us to unite them as "units of units." On subsequent levels of abstraction, the re-presentations of sensory-motor material of everyday experience (Piaget's "figurative" elements) drop out, and what remains is the purely "operative" (i.e., abstractions from operations).

None of this is developed in a free wholly arbitrary fashion. Every individual's abstraction of experiential items is constrained (and thus guided) by social interaction and the need of collaboration and communication with other members of the group in which he or she grows up. No individual can afford not to establish a relative fit with the consensual domain of the social environment.[12]

An analogous development takes place with regard to mathematics, but here the social interaction specifically involves those who are active in that field. The consensual domain into which the individual must learn to fit is that of mathematicians, teachers, and other adults insofar as they practice mathematics. The process of adaptation is the same as in other social domains, but there is an important difference in the way the degree of adaptation can be assessed. In the domain of everyday living, fit can be demonstrated by sensory-motor evidence of successful interaction (e.g., when an individual is asked to buy apples and returns with items that the other recognizes as apples). The only observable manifestation of the demand as well as of the response in the abstract reaches of the domain of mathematics are symbols of operations. The operations themselves remain unobservable. Understanding can therefore never be demonstrated by the presentation of results that may have been acquired by rote learning.[13] This is one of the reasons why mathematics teachers often insist (to the immense boredom of the students) on the exact documentation of the algorithm by means of which the result was obtained. The flaw in this procedure is that any documentation of an algorithm is again a sequence of symbols which in themselves do not demonstrate the speaker's or writer's understanding of the symbolized operations. Hence, the production of such a sequence, too, may be the result of rote learning.

Other contributions to this volume will illustrate how a constructivist approach to instruction deals with this problem. They will also show that the constructivist teacher does not give up his or her role as a guide—but this leadership takes the form of encouraging and orienting the students' constructive effort rather than curtailing their autonomy by presenting ready-made results as the only permitted path.

Here, I would merely stress the sharp distinction which, in my view, has to be made between teaching and training. The first aims at the students' conceptual fit with the consensual domain of the particular field, a fit which, from the teacher's perspective, constitutes understanding. The second aims at the students' behavioral fit which, from the teacher's perspective, constitutes acceptable performance. This is not to say that rote learning and the focus on adequate performance should have no place in constructively oriented instruction. But it does mean that, where the domain of mathematics is concerned, instruction that focuses on performance alone can be no better than trivial.

Concluding Remarks

If one seriously wants to adopt the radical constructivist orientation, the changes of thinking and of attitudes one has to make are formidable. It is also far from easy to maintain them consequentially. Much like physical habits, old ways of thinking are slow to die out and tend to return surreptitiously.

In everyday living, we don't risk much if we continue to speak of lovely sunsets and say that tomorrow the sun will rise at such and such a time—even though we now hold that it is the earth that moves and not the sun. Similarly, there is no harm in speaking of knowledge, mathematical and other, as though it had ontological status and could be "objective" in that sense; as a way of speaking, this is virtually inevitable in the social interactions of everyday life. But when we let scientific knowledge turn into belief and begin to think of it as unquestionable dogma, we are on a dangerous slope. The critics of Copernicus who argued that his system must be "wrong" because it denied that the earth is the center of the universe could not claim to be "scientific"—they argued in that way for political and religious reasons. Science, as Bellarmino pointed out, produces hypotheses, and, as such, they may or may not be useful. Their use may also be temporary. The science we have today holds that neither the earth nor the sun has a privileged position in the universe. Like the contemporary philosophers of science, constructivists have tried to learn from that development and to give up the traditional conception of knowledge as a "true" representation of an experiencer-independent state of affairs. That is why radical constructivism does not claim to have found an ontological truth but merely proposes a hypothetical model that may turn out to be a useful one.

Let me conclude with a remark that is not particularly relevant to the teaching of mathematics but might be considered by educators in general. Throughout the two thousand five hundred years of Western epistemology, the accepted view has been a realist view. According to it, the human knower can attain some knowledge of a really existing world and can use this knowledge to modify it. People tended to think of the world as governed by a God who would not let it go under. Then, faith shifted from God to science. The world that science was mapping was called "Nature" and was believed to be ultimately understandable and controllable. Yet, it was also believed to be so immense that mankind could do no significant harm to it. Today, one does not have to look far to see that this attitude has endangered the world we are actually experiencing.

If the view is adopted that "knowledge" is the conceptual means to make sense of experience, rather than a "representation" of something that is supposed to lie beyond it, this shift of perspective brings with it an important corollary: the concepts and relations in terms of which we perceive and conceive the experiential world we live in are necessarily generated by ourselves. In this sense, it is we who are responsible for the world we are experiencing. As I have reiterated many times, radical constructivism does not suggest that we can construct anything we like, but it does claim that within the constraints that limit our construction there is room for an infinity of alternatives. It, therefore, does not seem untimely to suggest a theory of knowing that draws attention to the knower's responsibility for what the knower constructs.

Notes

1. Vico's reply to his critics, included in the 2nd edition of *De Antiquissima Italorum Sapientia*, 1711; reprinted in Vico (1858) p. 143.

2. *De Antiquissima Italorum Sapientia*, Naples, 1710; reprinted with Italian translation, 1858.

3. *Giornale de'Letterati d'Italia*, 1711, vol.V, article VI; reprinted in Vico (1858), p. 137.

4. cf. Hermann Diels (1957), Xenophanes, fragment 34.

5. cf. Plato's "The Republic" in *Great Dialogues of Plato* (1956), p. 312ff., p.139.

6. Montaigne wrote this in his *Apologie de Raymond Sebond* (1575-76); cf Essais, 1972, vol. 2, p. 139.

7. Though most philosophers, today, would agree that the ontological realm is perceptually inaccessible, they balk at Kant's suggestion that it is also conceptually inaccessible to us. They are therefore still stuck with the paradox that they have no way of showing the truth of the ontological claims they make.

8. This reference was brought to my attention by a personal communication from Jacques Voneche (Geneva, 1985).

9. See, for instance, Kitchener's recent article (1989) on Piaget's early work on the role of social interaction and exchange.

10. Paul Feyerabend's recent comment (1987) on the famous letter Cardinal Bellarmino wrote in the context of Galileo's trial, makes this point in exemplary fashion: "To use modern terms: astronomers are entirely safe when saying that a model has predictive advantages over another model, but they get into trouble when asserting that it is therefore a faithful image of reality. Or, more generally: the fact that a model works does not by itself show that reality is structured like the model" (p. 250).

11. The focus on "operations of distinction" is a major contribution of Humberto Maturana's biological approach to cognition (1980a); the notion as such, however, is implicit in much of Piaget's work (e.g., his *Mechanisms of Perception*, 1969).

12. Lest this be interpreted as a concession to realism, let me point out that, in the constructivist view, the term "environment" always refers to the environment as experientially constructed by the particular subject, not to an "objective" external world.

13. Thinking, conceptual development, understanding, and meaning are located in someone's head and are never directly observable. A formidable confusion was generated by the behaviorist program that tried to equate meaning with observable response.

Chapter 3: Epistemology, Constructivism, and Discovery Learning in Mathematics

Gerald A. Goldin
Rutgers University

What is the best way to characterize the body of knowledge that we call mathematics? How do children and adults learn mathematics most effectively? How can we best study their learning processes, and assess the outcomes of learning? Can meaningful learning be consistently distinguished from nonmeaningful or rote learning? What constitutes effective mathematics teaching, and how can elementary and secondary school teachers be enabled to provide it?

In the accompanying papers, a number of my colleagues propose partial answers to these questions. Recurrent themes in these papers include the following: (1) a view of mathematics as *invented* or *constructed* by human beings, rather than as an independent body of "truths" or an abstract and necessary set of rules; (2) an interpretation of mathematical meaning as *constructed by the learner* rather than imparted by the teacher; (3) a view of mathematical learning as occurring most effectively through *guided discovery*, *meaningful application*, and *problem solving*, as opposed to imitation and reliance on the rote use of algorithms for manipulating formal symbols; (4) the study and assessment of learning through individual interviews and small-group case studies which go far beyond traditional paper-and-pencil tests of skills; (5) approaches to effective teaching through the creation of classroom *learning environments*, encouraging the development of diverse and creative problem-solving processes in students, and reducing the exclusive emphasis on mathematically correct responses; and (6) goals for teacher preparation and development which include reflections on *epistemology* consideration of the origins of mathematical knowledge, investigating and understanding mathematical knowledge as constructed and mathematical learning as a constructive process, and abstraction from teachers' and students' own mathematical problem-solving experiences.

This set of ideas, with which I strongly concur, has a long and distinguished history of development in mathematics education. It is to be hoped that the monograph will contribute

---

The ideas in this chapter evolved from discussions at the Conference on Models for Teacher Development in Mathematics, June 4-5, 1986, sponsored by the New Jersey Department of Higher Education and the Rutgers University Center for Mathematics, Science, and Computer Education. A brief version was presented at the 13th International Conference of PME in Paris (Goldin, 1989).

to their exposition and advancement, particularly at the present critical juncture—when, despite increasing recognition of the urgency of improving mathematics and science education, public policy in the United States and in many states remains uncertain of the most effective methods to adopt, and too often encourages movement in directions opposite to those described.

Recently, considerable attention has been devoted by the mathematics education research community to questions of epistemology as they pertain to the psychology of mathematics learning—particularly to the philosophical perspective known as *radical constructivism*. Many of those who have adopted a constructivist approach to learning and teaching base their theories on radical constructivist epistemology, which has emerged as offering a powerful justification for views such as those above (Cobb, 1981; Confrey, 1986; Steffe, von Glasersfeld, Richards, & Cobb, 1983; von Glasersfeld, 1984; 1987a). This essay is intended to raise some issues in criticism of our adopting radical constructivism as the foundation for our approach to mathematics education, even as I argue in favor of what I would prefer to call a "moderate constructivist" view. I hope to indicate how the six recurrent themes I have just listed can emerge from an empiricist epistemology that is consistent with scientific methods of inquiry as they are usually understood and applied, and that avoids some of the potentially damaging consequences of radical constructivism (Kilpatrick, 1987).

In offering the arguments which will follow, I nevertheless would like to stress at the outset my respect and admiration for the thinking of many individual researchers and mathematics educators of the radical constructivist school, including those who are authors of the accompanying papers. Their contribution has, in my opinion, been especially valuable as a challenge to the premature conclusions which are sometimes drawn from empirical, quantitative, and apparently "scientific" research in mathematics education. Such a challenge is particularly important when, as is often the case, the principal variables that have been selected for empirical study are surface variables selected because they are relatively easy to make quantitative, while more difficult cognitive variables are disregarded. Radical constructivists have also sought needed alternatives to the overly mechanical and deterministic models sometimes offered by the artificial intelligence/cognitive science school.

Epistemological Schools of Thought

Epistemology is the branch of philosophy that deals with the underpinnings of how we know what we know, and in particular the logical (and sometimes the psychological) bases for ascribing validity or "truth" to what we know. To place radical constructivism in context, let us consider on an elementary level some contrasting epistemological perspectives. I shall mention a few of the philosophical questions that these perspectives have addressed, and some of the implications for psychological research and educational practice that have been drawn from them—sometimes quite erroneously.

Most epistemological reasoning begins with an analysis of the sources of what "I" (the reasoner) know. One major source of knowledge is *via* my senses—the world of sensory experience or "sense-data," directly accessible to me. Such direct, "inner" experiences can be taken to include "feelings" as well as "sensations" (e.g., my experience of pleasure, as well as of warmth). Another possible source of knowledge is logical reasoning and introspection—hypotheses and/or conclusions which I can reach through mental processes. Some of the many questions with which epistemologists then grapple are the following:

Can I validly infer the existence of an external reality, apart from my own experience? If so, how? What can I know about it, if it exists, and how can I arrive at such knowledge?

Can I validly infer the existence of the internal experiences of other people? If so, how? What comparisons can be made between their internal experiences and my own?

Can I consistently verify the validity of my own logical reasoning processes? Are logical reasoning and mathematical reasoning in some sense intrinsically valid, are they merely social conventions adopted by a subset of human society, or are they essentially private and non-comparable between individuals?

What does it mean to say that a statement in mathematics is "true"? What does it mean to assert that an empirical statement in science is "true," one that seems to pertain to "external reality"? Is there any sense in which either of these "truths" is "objective?" Is the science we call psychology different in this respect from the physical and biological sciences because its domain includes "the mind?"

Over the centuries, radically different perspectives have been proposed by the exponents of various epistemological schools, leading to very different answers to such questions. The following brief, highly simplified overview is intended to convey the flavor of a few main approaches (see, e.g., Turner, 1967, for more detail at an introductory level).

Idealism is the view that all reality is, in fact, mental. All that I experience is mental, and no external, physical "real world" can be validly inferred from that experience. It is thus a rather extreme version of empiricism. But idealism broadly construed may allow for the existence of other minds, or even for a universal mind with which individual minds share experience. It is possible to be an idealist in one's metaphysics, but an epistemological realist. ***Solipsism*** is the still more radical view that the only reality is in *my* mind.

At the other end of the spectrum, ***causal realism*** is the view that the external world exists and in fact is what *causes* me to have the sense experiences that I have, although it is distinct from those experiences. This view falls within the more general framework of ***rationalism***, as it asserts that one can acquire knowledge about the physical world through reason and logical inference. Sensory experiences in this view are not very trustworthy. They play a role, but they may be misleading or illusory. They are not the most fundamental, ultimate reality; and one must reason one's way through them to arrive at knowledge of the external world.

Empiricism relies much more heavily on sense-data as the initial "givens" of epistemology. They are the elements of a world-as-experienced. Observation and measurement become fundamental processes for recording and organizing sense-data, and inferences drawn from patterns in sense-data account for the validity of knowledge. For example, the view that real-world statements about physical objects function as *useful summaries* of patterns in observed and predicted sensory experience is an empiricist perspective.

Many epistemologists have distinguished between "analytic" and "synthetic" truth, though they have not always agreed on their definitions, and the distinction itself has been questioned. Roughly speaking, analytic statements, such as "All brothers are siblings," are those that are true by virtue of the meanings or definitions of the terms involved and are not subject to empirical contradiction, whereas synthetic statements, such as "George Polya was a mathematician," depend for their truth on empirical evidence. Analytic statements may nevertheless require *reasoning* to verify them. One point of view is that mathematics itself consists of a body of analytic knowledge, while another (20th-century) view is that mathematics is in essence a purely formal symbol system, with an internal logic but without intrinsic content.

One of the more influential forms of ***radical empiricism***, known as ***logical positivism***, adopts the "verifiability criterion" of meaning, whereby the only meaningful content of a synthetic statement consists of the methods whereby it can in principle be confirmed or disconfirmed observationally.

Radical constructivism is a school of epistemology which emphasizes that we can never have access to a world of reality, only to the world that we ourselves construct out of our own experience. All knowledge, whether mathematical or not, is *necessarily* constructed. Without evidence for some form of telepathic perception, no individual has direct knowledge of anyone else's world of experience; we can only construct personal models of the knowledge and experience of others. Thus, one can never conclude that one's own knowledge is "the same as" that of another person. Likewise, we can only construct models of reality, and can never conclude that our own knowledge is in fact "knowledge of the real world."

In the radical constructivist view, knowledge about mathematics, science, psychology, or the everyday world is never *communicated*, but of epistemological necessity *constructed* (and reconstructed) by *unique individuals*. It is constructed out of our in-context experience of each other's speech and actions. Thus, social conventions and social interactions in contexts, rather than any more "absolute" criterion of "truth" or "objectivity," often function as the most important determinants of whether an individual's knowledge is regarded as valid, or whether a mathematical or scientific concept to be taught has been "correctly" learned. Constructivism in this sense is to be distinguished from an earlier use of the term to describe the intuitionist view that an existential assertion in mathematics (e.g., the existence of a set with certain properties) acquires meaning only by means of an effective construction (Lerman, 1989).

Two Sets of Epistemological Influences on Mathematics Education

At times each, school of epistemology has influenced research on the psychology of mathematics education, as well as classroom practices. Here I mention two such sets of influences. First we consider the impact of logical positivist views, which were partially responsible for the ascendancy of radical behaviorist psychology, and lent support to the "behavioral objectives" approach to mathematics education (Skinner, 1953; Mager, 1962; Sund & Picard, 1972). Then we explore some aspects of the current radical constructivist influence.

Logical Positivism

The idea in psychology that there exist mental states, knowable through direct experience, is quite compatible with idealist epistemology: since in the idealist view all reality is mental, there is no fundamental basis for distinguishing between *behavior* (or, in a more precisely idealist characterization, those mental experiences that are classified as behavior), and *mind* (or, the full set of mental experiences that I or other human beings have). These are on the same epistemological footing. Likewise, the causal realist who so inclines can posit the *reality* of minds—my mind and other minds—seeing them as in principle knowable through reasoning from their effects (on me, or on other observers): the mental states of others and of myself are simply a part of the external reality, belonging to the "world out there" that causes me to experience certain things (i.e., mental states are knowable in principle by reasoning from their effects). Thus, mentalistic explanations of behavior in psychology and characterizations of learning outcomes in education which are based on the presumed existence of mental states and mental faculties of students can at least be made compatible with either idealist or causal realist epistemological views.

The logical positivists, however, rejected such mentalistic explanations of behavior as *meaningless* in the sense of the verifiability criterion, involving in-principle-unobservable statements. The exclusive focus of the radical behaviorists on stimuli, on responses, and on empirically verifiable laws governing the relationships between them derived quite explicitly from the fact that stimulus situations and behavioral responses are directly *observable* and *measurable*, while presumed cognitive processes (or any other mental processes) are not. Thus, it was argued, the latter should be excluded *a priori* from psychology on epistemological grounds.

Likewise, the "behavioral objectives" approach to education (including mathematics education) was deemed to follow from necessary, "scientific" epistemological principles. These principles required that observable and measurable learning outcomes be specified in advance, in order that statements of the objectives of instruction satisfy the verifiability criterion of meaningfulness.

But reliance on behavioral objectives has not benefitted mathematics education, nor has stimulus-response psychology proved capable of describing insightful mathematics learning effectively. Often, the exclusively behavioral characterization of desirable learning outcomes leads educators to rely on the teaching of discrete, disconnected skills in mathematics, rather than on developing meaningful patterns, principles, and insights. Entire public school mathematics departments have devoted their summers to rewriting the objectives of their textbooks in behavioral terms, replacing non-operationally-verifiable words like "understand" with operationally verifiable words like "solve correctly."

One of the drawbacks of this approach is that once the mathematical behaviors to be tested are specified operationally, it usually seems most "efficient" to teach those behaviors as directly as possible, which may mean through rote rather than insightful processes. Computational speed and accuracy become ends in their own right, standardized paper-and-pencil tests come to dominate the instructional process, and teachers assert with surprising unanimity that they have no classroom time to spend on mathematical exploration, discovery learning, or problem solving.

There are, of course, those in society who advocate "back to basics" in mathematics not for epistemological reasons, but essentially for reasons of personal comfort and its compatibility with their personal values—people who extoll drill and practice for its own sake or for its presumed moral benefits, who argue for performance-based student and teacher accountability to achieve public policy objectives, or who are simply uneasy about school practices that encourage diversity and exploration. But even many behaviorists would acknowledge that the goals of speed and accuracy in routine mathematical computation and the methods of drill and practice, which most mathematics education researchers reject as at best inadequate and at worst deeply damaging, do not follow from any *a priori* epistemological principles of scientific method.

If we are to reject radical behaviorism as an epistemological basis for education, I believe that it is important to pinpoint the error in the positivist analysis, rather than simply rest content with deploring behaviorism's effects. It is not necessary to adopt radical constructivism to do this; one can argue effectively from a moderate empiricist perspective.

We can, in fact, go so far as to agree that meaningful synthetic statements should have in-principle-verifiable *implications*, without requiring such statements to be themselves immediately and directly verifiable. The moderate empiricist would not concede that the *only* meaning of a statement consists in its *presently* verifiable consequences. Thus, a model for cognition that makes use of unobservable entities (for example, internal cognitive representations) may succeed in *usefully summarizing and synthesizing observable events* (such as behaviors), and such a model may itself suggest *additional* observations that were not specified in advance. There is nothing at all unscientific about such models, particularly if they provide a more parsimonious description of observable phenomena than models based on directly observable entities such as stimuli and responses. Indeed, the early atomic theory in chemistry made use of entities (atoms and molecules) that were then *thought to be in principle unobservable* because they were too small ever to see, smaller than the wavelength of visible light; but the model accounted parsimoniously for a considerable variety of experimental observations (for example, observations that fit the law of multiple proportions). Later, scientists found additional consequences of the theory, and as it happened invented once-unforeseeable ways to observe atoms and molecules directly, such as the electron microscope. To have discarded the atomic theory as intrinsically meaningless based on the positivist argument would not have done justice to the theory, and would have set back the progress of chemistry quite substantially.

In fairness, we should note that the early behaviorists were reacting (at least in part) against particular mentalistic psychological theories derived largely from introspection, which bore little relationship to systematic empirical observation. Thus, in the course of time they did sweep away much that (unlike the early atomic theory) was relatively valueless scientifically. Nevertheless, the radical behaviorists' *a priori* epistemological reasoning was simply wrong, and it did a great deal of damage to educational practice in mathematics.

Radical Constructivism

In sharp contrast to logical positivism, the radical constructivist position not only allows but necessitates the construction in psychology of models for the cognitions or mental processes (i.e., the "understandings" of others). But radical constructivism has further consequences for psychology and for mathematics education. These consequences are very different from the implications of other epistemological points of view, and should be carefully considered. For example, there is the epistemological conclusion that all knowledge is constructed, and its corollary that all learning (including mathematics learning) involves constructive processes. According to the radical constructivist, these are not conclusions to be derived from controlled empirical studies of learners in which we might imagine one could *distinguish* observationally between constructive and non-constructive learning, and try to ascertain the occasions of their respective occurrence or the degrees of their effectiveness. Instead, it is claimed that they follow from fundamental, *a priori* epistemological considerations, in other words, the nature of human knowledge is that it is *necessarily* "constructed" out of the individual's world of experience, so that learning *necessarily* entails a process of construction.

In addition, radical constructivism maintains that each person's world of experience is context-dependent—unique to that individual, and by its very nature inaccessible to others. Thus, each individual's constructed knowledge is necessarily unique and contextually dependent. Again, these are not empirically based conclusions, but *a priori* epistemological necessities.

The conceptualization of a "mathematical structure" (such as the set of integers and their properties), or a category with structural properties (such as groups, rings, or integral domains), is natural to the mathematician and has been quite central to "structural" goals in mathematics teaching (Dienes, 1963; Dienes & Jeeves, 1965), as well as to some models for mathematics teacher development. Likewise, the "structure of a problem" or of a problem representation (the complexity of its search space, etc.), seen as *external* to learners and problem solvers, is important in task variable research (Goldin, 1984). But this perspective is challenged directly by radical constructivism, which denies us mathematical structures or structural problem descriptions as analytical tools apart from the constructed knowledge of a learner or problem solver. In the radical constructivist view there can *a priori* be no such thing as mathematical structure existing apart from an individual's constructed knowledge, nor can we talk meaningfully of a problem's structure apart from the understandings of a problem solver. Furthermore, there is—again, *a priori*—no way of knowing that a problem (or a mathematical concept) has the same structure for different individuals. This is *not* because it might be found empirically that each person constructs his or her knowledge differently; it is because radical constructivist epistemology does not *in principle* ever permit us to conclude that two individuals have "the same" knowledge.

Descriptive case studies then *must* replace controlled experimentation in the assessment of mathematical learning and teaching effectiveness, because the cognitions of individuals are simply not comparable. If we accept radical constructivism, case study research in mathematics education is not merely a technique that facilitates an exploratory stage of empirical inquiry, it is the best that can in principle be achieved when epistemology is taken into account, and it must *replace* controlled experimentation in research.

Finally, the radical constructivist may argue that the views of mathematics, mathematical meaning, and effective mathematics education mentioned in the introduction above, follow from the application of constructivist epistemological principles to consideration of the nature of mathematical knowledge.

It is interesting to note that in developing and arguing for the above ideas, radical constructivists are not in particularly close agreement with Piaget, from whom they trace their lineage. Piaget not only recognized "logical necessity," but also accorded an important role to "structure" apart from idiosyncratic construction by individuals (Piaget, 1970d). Of course, Piaget, too, became a major influence in stemming the radical behaviorist tide.

Although the direction of the radical constructivist influence on mathematics education has been diametrically opposite to that of the logical positivist influence, there seems to me to be a certain parallel—in that researchers of both schools claim that their view derives from necessary epistemological principles, rather than from empirical research. But why should we be concerned about or disturbed by the epistemological underpinnings, if we agree with the general direction of the radical constructivist influence? I think that there are two dangers we may face should it turn out that the reasoning of the radical constructivists is fundamentally incorrect.

First, those of us who advocate meaningful mathematics learning through constructive, discovery processes may find that some invalid or unhelpful conclusions and beliefs consequent to the epistemological reasoning have become intertwined with otherwise valid perspectives. Secondly, it may happen that an extremely important and timely body of ideas about what mathematics learning and teaching can and should be—ideas which are *non-behavioristic* and *non-mechanistic*—may be rendered invalid in the eyes of those who (with justification) seek an empirical, scientific basis for mathematics education research. Indeed, in recent scholarly debate, disagreements on important and controversial issues affecting policy (such as the identification of variables associated with effective classroom practices) have been framed as differences between quantitative empiricist and constructivist epistemological analyses (Brophy, 1986a, 1986b; Confrey, 1986). As Kilpatrick (1987, pp. 11-12) noted, "in some [constructivist] writings the implication seems to be drawn that certain teaching practices and views about instruction presuppose a constructivist view of knowledge. That implication is false." It is important to recognize that one does not need to accept radical constructivist epistemology in order to adopt a model of learning as a constructive process, or to advocate increased classroom emphasis on guided discovery in mathematics. We shall see that a scientific, moderately empiricist epistemology is equally compatible with such views.

Constructive and Non-Constructive Learning

Before addressing the epistemological questions raised by radical constructivists, let us consider the difference between constructive and non-constructive models for learning in some fairly well-understood situations. To do so, I here define "learning" broadly as *the acquisition by a system or entity of a set of in-principle, observable competencies or capabilities.* I shall contrast two situations where empirical models are appropriate, but, because in both cases the system involved is not the human mind, we are not immediately embroiled in sensitive epistemological questions.

For the first example, consider the process whereby a computer acquires competencies as it is programed in a higher-level language such as BASIC to carry out a sequence of operations. The user, typically unfamiliar with the detailed circuitry of the machine, needs a *useful model* for what is happening; and even detailed and highly accurate knowledge of the machine's circuitry would not be especially useful to the typical BASIC programmer. The desired model is provided simply by assuming that as a consequence of the input of a program, the computer represents internally the procedures and contingencies that, in the program, are expressed by means of a conventional notational system, and that the machine follows precisely those procedures when instructed to execute the program. Thus, the computer "learns" by representing procedural instructions, and it displays its newly acquired competencies by executing them. For practical purposes, the learning is adequately modeled by *non-constructive* processes, a process we might loosely call *literal transcription.* Although we have not described in detail the *way* in which the actual internal representation takes place as the program is entered, there is a useful sense in which we can say that no new, important, internal representational systems are being built while this is happening. The new competencies that will be acquired are limited to procedures that are fully described by the program itself.

In contrast, consider a conventional model for the body's acquisition of immunity to a disease through inoculation. The body somehow "learns" to protect itself against an invading virus (in the sense of acquiring the capability of doing so effectively) through infection with a killed or weakened virus. In developing a vaccine, medical scientists may not know in detail the procedures by which the body will eventually be able to fend off the virus. Thus, they cannot provide the body directly with a set of biochemical procedures to follow. Certainly the biological "learning" process that takes place as a consequence of immunization is *not* adequately modeled as the representation of any set of explicit instructions provided by doctors or scientists. Instead, it is more useful to conjecture that through its interaction with the weakened or killed virus, the immune system *constructs* the capability of recognizing the dangerous virus biochemically and of manufacturing antibodies more rapidly or in greater quantity than it could otherwise have done. It is worth noting that the "knowledge" constructed still consists of *procedures*. We are not drawing a distinction between procedural *versus* conceptual knowledge, but one between constructive and non-constructive learning processes. Here the "learning" is modeled constructively. The nature of the constructed capabilities is complex and not fully understood, though the evidence for such a model is obtained through controlled, empirical, scientific research.

In these examples, it is evident that one need not have recourse to arguments from radical constructivist epistemology in order to justify, on empirical grounds, a distinction between "constructive" and "non-constructive" models for learning. Either type of model may apply, depending on the situation. The dual hypotheses that the immune system makes use of constructive processes while the computer represents the program input literally or transcriptively are not at all dependent on radical constructivist epistemology—it would not be very helpful to immunology (or to computer science) to say that "the immune system (or the computer) has direct access only to its own world of experience, which is unique and not directly comparable with that of any other immune system (or computer), or that of the scientist (or programmer)." Nor need the computer programmer adopt a causal realist perspective in order to arrive at a useful transcriptive model. Instead, the hypotheses depend for their tenability on the empirical observations of the biologist, together with his available theoretical models of cellular biology and biochemistry, and on the empirical observations of the computer programmer, together with her knowledge of computer design.

Likewise, the modeling of mathematics learning by students through constructive processes need not rely on radical constructivist underpinnings. The hypothesis that the "construction" of knowledge by human beings takes place—possibly involving several developmental stages—when offered as part of a scientific theory of competence acquisition is *logically independent* of radical constructivist epistemology. It is quite possible that some learning is constructive and some is not. It is possible that the two can be distinguished empirically. One may even hypothesize that constructive learning processes are more effective, leading to wider generalizability of the knowledge, improved retention, a greater likelihood that the knowledge will be transferred to unfamiliar problem-solving situations, and so forth.

To paraphrase this conclusion, one does not have to be a radical constructivist in order to advocate discovery learning, divergent thinking, and open-ended problem solving in mathematics education. The moderate empiricist is equally capable of rejecting radical behaviorism, of taking account of contextual influences on learning, and of recognizing the existence and importance of individual differences in student cognitions—in mathematics, science, or any other field of education.

Constructivist and Non-Constructivist Views of Knowledge

It is important to try to pinpoint and make explicit the source of the philosophical disagreement between the moderate empiricist position I am advocating here and the epistemological reasoning of the radical constructivists. To do this I must return to the question of how "I" (the reasoning entity) acquire knowledge.

Let us accept as valid the radical constructivist statement that I have direct access only to *my* "world of experience." This statement is quite different from the phraseology sometimes seen, that *we* have direct access only to *our* worlds of experience. The latter phrasing is invalid, in that it tacitly places the reasoning entity ("me") on the same epistemological footing as other human minds, but presumably not on the same footing as computers or biological systems.

From my world of experience, my sense-data, etc., it is valid and reasonable to assert that I *construct* (in the epistemological sense) my "knowledge." In the course of this construction, I *infer* (tacitly, and later overtly) a "real world" that displays regularities. I also *reason* with words and symbols drawn from experience, including mathematical symbols, and I relate these to the real world that I have myself constructed.

As an empiricist, I then reason about it all: I might now consider the statements that I make about the "real world" to be on closer examination useful summaries of patterns in my experiences, in sense-data both actual and contingent. (Were I a realist, I might prefer to *assume* such a world to exist objectively and then infer that it is the cause of my experiences.) Whichever approach I take, within the "real world" that I have inferred (or assumed) are inferred entities called "other people." It is now an additional and major epistemological step for me to reason that other people also have "worlds of experience." This is a step that might enable me to organize *my* experience of their behavior; people *seem* to act *as if* they are experiencing sensations, feelings, and thoughts somewhat like my own.

When as an empiricist I seek to model the cognitions of other people (for example, students or teachers), to characterize their knowledge for the purpose of better teaching them mathematics, I must begin with my *own* experiences and ultimately infer something about *their* knowledge. To some extent, I can do this informally. But to be systematic about it I need the techniques of empirical science—*because, the behavior and cognitions of others are, for me, on the same epistemological footing as any other aspect of the real world* (such as the behavior and structure of atoms and molecules).

The fact that it is cognition that I wish to study, rather than physics or chemistry, contributes in only a limited way to the epistemological underpinnings of my investigative methodology. In the scientific study of cognition (unlike the physical sciences) it may be helpful to me to establish and reason from: (a) correspondences between the behavior of other people and my own behavior, and (b) correspondences between my own behavior and my own subjective experiences. In my everyday interactions, I inevitably make use of such correspondences. But this technique does have severe limitations: (a) it is empirically evident that other people differ from me behaviorally in important respects, and (b) there is empirical evidence that my awareness and recollections of my own behavior and of my subjective experiences are imperfect. Thus, reasoning about other people's cognitions by analogy with my own will be at best a heuristic tool. It may guide some of my theorizing, and may motivate some of my everyday teaching activities, but it must yield to more rigorous empirical investigation when the latter is possible.

In particular, I would argue that it is epistemologically incorrect to regard as equivalent the following two senses of the term "knowledge": (1) the "knowledge" or cognitions of other people that I (or other researchers) are trying to describe or hope to model when we study cognition empirically, and (2) the inner "knowledge" of the epistemological "I" that we have been discussing, the "knowledge that I construct from my world of experience." These two senses of the word "knowledge" refer to different things. The former refers to a *shared construct* of the knowledge of other individuals—of students and teachers—a well-defined and optimally useful *empirical* construct that can ultimately enable researchers to better predict and influence the mathematical behavior of students and teachers. The latter is accessible only to introspection, constructed by me from a world of experience that is inaccessible to others.

Thus, what we seek is a set of tools for predicting and affecting learning that can be tested empirically, improved, and shared, and which all of us can use to become better mathematics educators. Whether such an empirically-based theory "really" succeeds in describing an individual's inner knowledge-as-constructed (assuming such to exist) is never an issue, because that was not our intent.

The Nature of Mathematics, the Psychology of Learning, and Teacher Development

If we do not accept radical constructivism, it is reasonable to ask what we can infer from a moderate empiricist epistemology that has a bearing on teacher development, the major issue of this book. Let me close this paper with some suggestions.

What a teacher thinks mathematics is may greatly affect his or her approach to it in the classroom. Is it a body of absolute truth, or a set of arbitrary conventions? Is mathematics discovered or invented? Is it a set of rules and structures that exist apart from the individual, or does each person have his or her own set? What is the relation between mathematics and experience with non-mathematical entities, such as physical objects?

In the 19th and 20th centuries, two major developments in mathematics itself challenged the traditional notion of mathematics as a body of truths about the real world. First, there was the divorce of mathematics as a formal system from that which it describes. Thus, Euclidean and non-Euclidean geometries could *both* be mathematically valid, though in their usual interpretation they do not both describe the same physical universe. This development led to a new view of mathematics—no longer as a system of absolute truth, but as a *formal symbol-system*: a set of essentially arbitrary axioms and rules of inference, together with the theorems that can be derived from the axioms using the inferencing procedures. The second development was Gödel's result that for mathematical systems of sufficient complexity (such as the system of natural numbers), neither completeness nor a proof of consistency could ever be obtained. This result was reached by the technique of letting the symbol system of mathematics model *itself* so that numbers could be assigned to axioms and to theorems (about numbers). Taken together, these two developments epitomize both the triumphs and the logical limitations of formalism (Kline, 1980).

Thus, mathematics may be viewed *logically* as a set of assumed conventions for manipulating symbols. Once the conventions and rules of inference have been established, there is now a sense—contrary to the spirit of radical constructivism—in which the system *exists* , in which it "has" a structure, apart from any individual mathematician or student. That is, we may say that the rules and inferencing procedures were (historically) *invented,* and we may say that they are (psychologically) reconstructed and reinvented by individuals; but what follows from them once they have been established is *constrained* and longer arbitrary. Furthermore, the resulting structure must remain (in a logical sense) incomplete.

What is sometimes forgotten in the exclusive reliance on formalism, and what the empiricist stresses, is that mathematical rules are *motivated* by (empirical) experiences. For example, the commutative property of addition is *assumed* in a certain formal approach to number theory, but it can be *discovered* by children who have been encouraged to interpret addition in certain ways—for example, as a physical procedure that involves joining the elements of two sets of objects, and counting the number of elements in the resulting set.

It is, however, difficult to talk about *discovering* something, such as a pattern or a structure, if we are unwilling to regard it as "there," existing apart from the individual. Thus, the radical constructivist standpoint is of limited usefulness here. Sometimes we see expressed in a constructivist context the idea that children can *reinvent* mathematics; and one can easily imagine guiding children to "invent" the counting of objects and the operation of addition based on joining two sets of objects and counting the resulting set. But having done this, having invented the operation of addition, there now is an important sense in which the commutative property of addition is not something to be "invented." It already *exists* in the situation and is "there to be discovered," apart from the cognition of the individual child (who may or may not discover it). If the child is to be guided to make the discovery, it is obviously helpful for the teacher not only to be aware of the existence of such a property, but also to be able to present situations in which it emerges as a regularity or pattern to be detected and interpreted.

In encouraging *meaningful* rather than *rote* learning of mathematics, it is important that we develop teachers who can distinguish *empirically* between the two. One component of such an empirical distinction focuses on teaching and learning strategies. Teachers should be able to characterize, implement, and evaluate critically a range of approaches, from those in which the teacher states and exemplifies rules, to those in which the student detects patterns in situations, and formulates and verifies conjectures. Over reliance on the statement and exemplification of rules by the teacher is an ingredient in "rote" processes; while techniques involving student-detected patterns and the investigation of conjectures are ingredients of "meaningful" processes.

Another component is the empirical exploration of some of the possible (observable) capabilities of a child who has "learned" a rule such as the commutative property of addition.

Can the child . . . state the rule? . . . apply the rule to numerical examples when asked to do so? . . . apply the rule spontaneously to numerical examples? . . . identify instances of the rule when they are presented? . . . provide exemplars and non-exemplars when requested? All of these are, of course, important competencies, pertaining mainly to formal computation—yet they are competencies which in some classrooms might be acquired through rote, relatively non-meaningful (and non-constructive) procedures. Other capabilities suggest more meaningful learning. Can the child . . . illustrate the rule with physical objects? . . . give one or more reasons why the rule is true? . . . set up a pattern (using objects or using numbers) through which the rule can be discovered? The latter capabilities go beyond computation; they involve connections between numerical symbols and non-numerical domains, and they make explicit reference to reasoning processes as well as products.

Why do so many teachers, from the elementary school to the university, approach mathematical instruction in terms of stating and exemplifying rules and procedures, rather than from a guided discovery standpoint? There are numerous reasons. Some teachers, often (but not always) those with the least mathematical preparation, see mathematics *only* as such a set of rules and procedures. Some are insecure with their own mathematical ability, and find reassurance in procedures and algorithms that can be implemented in a fairly mechanical but at least a reliable way. At the other extreme there are college professors of unusually high mathematical ability who, perhaps because of that very ability, reason extraordinarily rapidly and tacitly. Thus, they may themselves be unaware of the complexity of their pattern-recognition, visualization, and problem-solving heuristics, and may describe their reasoning in terms of its overt product—an efficient and effective procedure. Many teachers, at all levels, are overly concerned with students' efficiency in arriving at solutions to problems. It takes less time to *state* a well-established method than it does to guide students to its discovery, and the stated method *appears* to take care of the set of problems at hand. And, of course, the prevailing emphasis on skills tests influences many teachers toward the short-term goal of teaching rote procedures.

It is, in my opinion, an *empirical* fact, not an epistemological necessity, that for large numbers of students at all levels of mathematics education methods involving the statement and application of rules (i.e., methods based on a *transcriptive* model) are less successful than methods involving of mathematical discovery (i.e., methods based on a *constructive* learning model). Rejection of the radical form of constructivism must *not* be taken as support for a return to behaviorism or rule-governed learning in mathematics. Rather, we must develop new empirical models for competence in mathematics that encompass much more complex capabilities, based on cognitions that can be characterized (empirically) as constructed by the learner through guided discovery processes (Goldin, 1987).

PART TWO

THE NATURE OF MATHEMATICS AND HOW IT IS LEARNED

Chapter 4: Children's Mathematical Learning: A Cognitive View

Arthur J. Baroody
University of Illinois
at Urbana-Champaign

Herbert P. Ginsburg
Teachers College
Columbia University

To promote meaningful learning, teachers must know how to tailor instruction so that it meshes with children's thinking (e.g., Brownell, 1935; NCTM, 1989; Dewey, 1963; Piaget, 1970c). Over the last 20 years, cognitive psychologists have made significant strides in understanding children's mathematical thinking (e.g., see Baroody, 1987a; Carpenter, Moser, & Romberg, 1982; Davis, 1984; Fuson, 1988; Gelman & Gallistel, 1978; Ginsburg, 1983, 1989; Hiebert, 1986; Lesh & Landau, 1983; Resnick & Ford, 1981; Steffe, von Glasersfeld, Richards, & Cobb, 1983). This body of knowledge promises to make a significant impact on educational practices. This chapter highlights key findings and implications of this important area of research.

Informal Mathematics

Preschool Mathematics: The Case of Alison[1]

Alison, just 5 years old and about to enter kindergarten, was playing a "basketball" game with her dad. With each score, her father announced "That's two!" After a handful or so of consecutive "baskets," Alison got another "two" and decided to keep track of her score. She arbitrarily concluded that her previous score was 11 and counted: "1, 2, 3, 4, 5, 6, 7, 8, 9, 10, 11 (short pause), 14, 17."

She got the next two points also and gleefully began to tally her score: "1, 2, 3, 4, 5, 6, 7, 8, 9, 10, 11 (pause), 14, 17." After a moment's thought, she exclaimed: "No, that's what I had!" She then proceeded to correct herself: "1, 2, 3, 4, 5, 6, 7, 8, 9, 10, 11, 14, 17, 16, 19."

Research Findings

The vignette of Alison illustrates a number of the key findings of a cognitive psychology of mathematical learning. It is clear that children develop their own (informal) mathematical knowledge—even before they receive any formal training in school. Cognitive research

---

Preparation of this chapter was supported, in part, by grant number MDR-847091 from the National Science Foundation.

(Baroody, 1987a; Fuson & Hall, 1983; Gelman & Gallistel, 1978; Ginsburg, 1989; Starkey & Gelman, 1982) indicates that, like Alison, preschoolers learn and apply a surprising amount of mathematics and enter school equipped and willing to learn more (e.g., Resnick, 1983).

Children's informal mathematics is based largely on counting. For example, Alison attempted to solve the arithmetic problem 11 and 2 more by counting up to 11 and then counting on from there twice more.

Informal mathematics involves active construction, not merely passive absorption of information. No one showed Alison how to compute sums mentally by counting. For example, she *reasoned* that "seventeen and two more" had to be larger than seventeen—specifically, two numbers (counts) beyond seventeen. Her addition strategy was the product of invention, not imitation.

Children develop and apply informal mathematics because it is personally meaningful, interesting, and useful to them. No one required or bribed Alison to tally her scores: devise an addition strategy and use it to compute sums. She actively applied her intelligence to solve a problem that was important to her.

Though surprisingly powerful, informal mathematics has its limitations. Although Alison understood that the number sequence could be used to calculate sums, her mental addition was restricted to small numbers. That is, she probably could have accurately computed the sum of nine and two but failed to do so for eleven and two more or seventeen and two more,[2] because she had not yet mastered the standard sequence beyond eleven.[3] Moreover, from an adult's perspective, Alison's methods are not the most logical or efficient. For instance, even after just figuring out that eleven and two more is seventeen, she solved seventeen and two more *by returning to one and counting up to seventeen again* (and only then added two more: "16, 19")!

Personal Mathematics of School Children

As we will see in this section, even after children begin school they continue to rely on their informal mathematics.

Invented Procedures

Indeed, cognitive research reveals that children often do not do mathematics the way it is taught (e.g., Davis, 1984; Ginsburg, 1989). That is, children do not simply imitate and quickly adopt adult strategies or patterns of thought (Brownell, 1935). For example, despite the emphasis in many schools on memorizing the number facts, children persist in computing (e.g., Baroody, 1985; Carpenter & Moser, 1984). In fact, regardless of mathematics curriculum, community, or country, children (initially) rely on counting to compute sums, differences, and products (e.g., Ginsburg, Posner, & Russell, 1981; Ginsburg & Russell, 1981; Kouba, 1986). The case of 9-year-old Sarita (S) illustrates the ineffectiveness of imposing knowledge on children and the power of their self-invented procedures.[4]

S: [Sarita writes 12 x 9 =, pauses, and says] My teacher told me a trick.

I: Yeah, what's the trick?

S: I think I can remember it ...Twelve, you take away one which is 11? [She writes the numeral 11 just above her numeral 12.] Um ...um [a long pause] I don't remember.

I: Um-hum. Suppose you didn't know at all what something like that is, okay? Twelve times nine ... I mean, never mind the teacher's trick now ... and you wanted to find out how much it was? Okay? And you could do anything you want with paper and pencil. How would you go about doing that?

S: Well...if I didn't know how to times?

I: Yeah.

S: I would add twelve nines.

I: Okay, that's one way of doing it. So, go ahead.

S: [Sarita writes 12 nines in a column (one beneath the other).] Um... um...four times nine is 36, so this is already 36. [She blocks off the first four nines, writes 36 in the box, and—while blocking off the next four nines—says:] Thirty-six and 36 is ... um ... 72. So this is 72, isn't it?

I: Is it?

S: Wait...um...["She goes back to the first set of nines and says:] Thirty-six. Yeah. [She writes the numeral 72 in the second box.]

I: Okay, good. So that's 72 you've got there, altogether, right?

S: Yeah. Um, 72 plus 36 [referring to the last four nines], um ... [She then uses the written renaming procedure to compute the sum and announces:] It's 108.

Self-regulated Learning

Children actively monitor and adjust their behavior. For instance, they invent increasingly efficient strategies to compute sums and differences (e.g., Baroody, 1987b; Carpenter & Moser, 1984; Groen & Resnick, 1977) and, in time, demonstrate flexibility by choosing from among their strategies the most efficient (e.g., Siegler, 1987; Siegler & Shrager, 1984; Woods, Resnick, & Groen, 1975). Consider the case of Mike who, despite his classification as mentally handicapped, could intelligently choose among his informal addition strategies to minimize his computational effort.[5] Given the problem 5 + 4, Mike *counted out* five fingers on one hand and four on another. He then began with one again and counted all the fingers put up to determine the sum. Later, he was given a problem with smaller addends (2 + 3) and solved it using well known finger patterns. *Without counting*, he put up two fingers on one hand and three on the other. Then he counted the fingers to determine the sum as he had done for 5 + 4. On a later trial, he was given 2 + 8. He quickly recognized that he did not have enough fingers on his right hand to represent the second addend and so he resorted to an invented procedure. First, he put out two fingers to represent the smaller addend. He then began with one, counted the eight fingers, and continued his count with "9, 10," as he pointed to the fingers put up previously. On another problem (1 + 7), he did not bother to use his fingers at all. He simply counted from one to seven and then once more.

Intrinsic Motivation

Children are naturally curious. They have an inherent drive to make sense of their environment and to cope with it. They are naturally inclined to search out patterns and relationships. School children rely on informal arithmetic procedures because these methods allow them to cope with their environment in a sensible manner, not because they are rewarded or reinforced. (Indeed, too often children are ridiculed or punished if they are caught counting.)

This does not mean that they will be interested in mathematics instruction regardless of how it is taught. For example, compare Aaron's disinterest in his first-grade instruction with the enthusiasm of his informal observation that single-digit number facts repeat themselves with larger numbers.[6]

I: How do you like math this year?

A: [Aaron (A) shrugs his shoulders unenthusiastically.]

I: What are you learning about in math?

A: [Without interest.] I'm not sure. We have to draw lines and junk like that.

I: Oh, you're matching sets to see if they're equal.

A: I guess. [Then his whole demeanor is transformed by a surge of enthusiasm.] Do you know how much 1,000 plus 1,000 is? It's 2,000!

I: Wow! Did you learn that in math class?

A: No, I'm just smart!

Surprising Strengths

Children exhibit surprising informal strengths. For example, they have previously unsuspected problem-solving skills (e.g., Carpenter, 1986; Carpenter & Moser, 1982; Riley,

Greeno & Heller, 1983). Even kindergartners and first-graders can solve simple addition and subtraction word problems by using counting strategies that model the meaning of a problem. Consider the case of Raul, a 6-year-old first grader:[7]

I: Raul, "Rabbit has 3 carrots. Squirrel has 5 carrots...." So, how much are three carrots and five carrots altogether?

R: [Raul (R) sits up, puts out both hands, and "hums" to himself while putting out his fingers. On his left hand he counts out three fingers, and on his right hand he immediately puts out all five. He pauses, looks at all of his fingers, some of which are moving very slightly, and announces:] Eight. [He then puts his hands down.]

I: Eight, okay. Now we have a different thing here, okay? Now, "rabbit has five carrots, and squirrel has three carrots." How many carrots do they have altogether?

R: [Raul holds out his left hand immediately with all five fingers and says:] Five. [He then holds up his right hand, puts out three fingers and says:] Three. [He looks at all of the fingers held out on his left hand, and then over at his right hand, as if counting his fingers altogether. He pushes both hands together and says:] Hmmm. [and starts over again with the left hand. This time, there is slight movement of each finger as he counts from his left hand to his right. He announces:] Eight. [and folds his hands.]

Limitations

Clearly, children's informal mathematics is not as complete, coherent, and logical as an adult's systematic knowledge (e.g., Baroody & Ginsburg, 1986; Cobb, 1985; Piaget, 1965). Note that Raul above uses his fingers to calculate five and three despite the fact that he has just determined that the sum of three and five is eight. Raul modeled each problem as he heard it and did not make use of the fact that 3 + 5 = 5 + 3 —that addition is commutative.

Consider the even more curious case of Casey (Baroody & Gannon, 1984). Though the kindergartner would disregard addend order to compute the sum of, say, 3 + 6 (*"1, 2, 3, 4, 5, 6; 7 is one more, 8 is two more, 9 is three more"*), he did not believe that it was equivalent in sum to 6 + 3. For example, shown 6 + 4 = 10 and 4 + 6 = written directly below it, Casey concluded that 4 + 6 would *not* add up to 10. Though disregarding addend order makes the task of calculating easier, it did not imply an understanding of the commutative principle.

Systematic Errors

Because the knowledge they construct is incomplete or inaccurate, children make systematic errors. Consider the case of 3-year-old Arianne:[8]

Father: Alright Arianne, what comes after '27, 28, 29' when we count?

Arianne: Tenty.

Tenty? This is not an imitated term that she has heard from her parents, Sesame Street, books, or her older siblings (e.g., her older sister by 18 months counted "... 27, 28, 29, twenty-ten"). It is a term she has *constructed* based on the *patterns* she has discerned in the counting sequence. Ten follows nine, so the term after "29" must have a ten in it. The twenties, unlike the single-digit and teen terms, all end in "ty"; so it follows that the next term, which in the girl's mind is a twenty term, should also end in "ty." The invented term tenty is a product of the child's incomplete knowledge of the counting patterns. Systematic errors, then, are evidence of a child's active attempts to make sense of the world and provide a window to the child's thinking.

Formal Mathematics

Formal mathematics, which is taught in school and which uses written symbols, can greatly extend children's ability to deal with quantitative issues. Indeed, the mathematical skills and concepts taught in the primary grades are not only the foundation for learning more advanced mathematics later in school but are basic "survival skills" in our technologically-oriented society. This formal mathematics is powerful in various ways. It is a highly precise and logical body of knowledge. Written procedures greatly increase calculation efficiency, especially with larger quantities, and provide a long-lasting record. However, the extent to which children benefit from formal instruction depends on how well it meshes with their thinking.

Assimilation

Children do not merely absorb or make a mental copy of new information; they assimilate it. That is, children filter and interpret new information in terms of their existing knowledge (e.g., Piaget, 1964). Children (and adults) cannot assimilate new information that is completely unfamiliar. Quite naturally, they quickly lose interest in the incomprehensible information and tune it out. Somewhat unfamiliar information can be related to existing knowledge and assimilated. Children are naturally interested in "moderately novel" information.

Assimilation and interest, then, go hand in hand. Like adults, young school children often do not make the effort to assimilate new information unless it makes some sense and hence is important to them. When a task piques their curiosity, children will spend considerable time and effort working at and reflecting upon it.

The cognitive principle of assimilation implies that understanding cannot be imposed upon children. It evolves as they actively try to make sense of the world. Meaningful learning occurs when children are actively engaged intellectually and emotionally. It occurs when they encounter moderately novel situations that excite their natural curiosity.

Informal Mathematics: A Basis for Assimilating Formal Mathematics

Though formal mathematics can greatly extend their capabilities, cognitive theory proposes children cannot immediately comprehend abstract instruction. For children to learn school mathematics in a meaningful manner, they must be given the opportunity to assimilate it. For primary children, this means interpreting school-taught instruction in terms of their relatively concrete informal knowledge. Mathematical symbols, computational algorithms (step-by-step procedures), and so forth can make sense to children *if* it is connected to their existing, personal, counting-based knowledge of mathematics.

Indeed, cognitive research indicates that, with any mathematical content, learners progress developmentally from concrete to abstract thinking (e.g., Crowley, 1987; Lunkenbein, 1985). That is, for a first grader learning to do written addition or a college student learning calculus, knowledge begins imprecisely with the apparent. This intuitive knowledge is highly concrete, spotty, and unsystematic (e.g., Ginsburg, 1982; Lunkenbein, 1985). In time, they master informal knowledge, which is more abstract but not entirely complete and systematic. With this basis, they can then acquire formal knowledge, which is relatively abstract, complete, and coherent. Only gradually, then, does knowledge in any domain become relatively complete, systematic, and logical.

Gaps

A gap between formal instruction and a child's existing knowledge prevents assimilation. It can make school-taught skills and concepts seem foreign and difficult to children. Indeed, a gap between children's relatively concrete informal mathematics and relatively abstract formal instruction for which they are not ready is a key reason for learning difficulties (Ginsburg, 1989; Hiebert, 1984).

The Direct-instruction Model

Formal mathematical instruction, even at the elementary level, does not suit children's thinking because it is too often based on a direct-teaching-and-practice model. That is, it involves a tell-show-do approach:

1. Instruction begins by *telling* a class what they need to know. Often, the teacher verbally explains the lesson. Sometimes the students are supposed to get the new information by reading their textbook.

2. Then the lesson is illustrated with examples. For example, the teacher may show how to do a procedure on the chalkboard. The procedure may be illustrated further by examples and illustrations in the textbook.

3. The children then imitate the teacher and practice the fact or procedure until it is automatic. Doing mathematics basically entails practice with written exercises: manipulating written symbols to obtain the correct answers. Predicated on the assumption that "practice makes perfect," students are regularly given extensive written assignments (e.g., Moyer & Moyer, 1985). Such an approach frequently overlooks the crucial developmental process of assimilation and the key developmental issue of readiness.

Abstract Instruction

With a direct instruction approach, new information is often too abstract for children to assimilate. If the use of objects and counting are not discouraged entirely, they are usually allowed only briefly when introducing arithmetic, place value, and so forth. Unfortunately, a highly verbal approach to instruction frequently is not meaningful to children—even when accompanied by pictures and demonstrations. When instruction fails to link written symbols and the manipulations involving these symbols to existing (informal) knowledge, it makes little or no sense to children (e.g., Davis, 1984). Heavy doses of practice with exercises that seem pointless to children further deaden interest and thinking. In brief, if children do not see a connection between the information presented in school and their existing mathematical knowledge, a lesson, in effect, falls on deaf ears. If children see no point in their written exercises, they approach them without thought and dispense with them as quickly as possible (e.g., Holt, 1964).

The case of Ronnie illustrates how a gap between abstract instruction and children's informal mathematics can prevent understanding and critical thinking.[9] An interviewer gave his nephew Ronnie, a first grader (age 7) at the time, this subtraction problem:

$$\begin{array}{r} 200 \\ \underline{-87} \end{array}$$

Though he had just completed successfully a series of simpler subtraction problems that required him to borrow once (e.g., 131 - 8 = ?), this problem completely stumped him. The interviewer asked if he learned to "borrow" in school. Ronnie indicated that he had; so the interviewer set out to explain how to solve the problem using a double-borrowing procedure. As the interviewer was his uncle, Ronnie listened politely to the explanation. However, after repeated demonstrations and explanations of the procedure, it was clear he did not grasp it. Mercifully, it was soon time to break for lunch. At the lunch table, the interviewer complimented Ronnie on his math. To which he replied, "But I can't do 200 - 87." Ronnie's father, a mathematics teacher, related the problem to Ronnie's existing knowledge (addition) with excellent results.

F: [Father (F) asks:] How many do you need to get from 87 to 90?

R: [Ronnie (R) responds:] Three.

F: How many do you need to get from 90 to 100?

R: Ten.

F: How many do you need to get from 100 to 200?

R: 100.

F: How many do you need to get from 87 to 200?

R: [Ronnie puzzled for a moment, says:] 113! That's the easy way!

Lockstep Instruction

Too often, a direct-instruction approach overlooks individual readiness, moves too quickly, and thus prevents assimilation of new information. With reading instruction, there is usually an effort made to tailor instruction to children's readiness, their rate of progress, and their individual learning style. Reading instruction often takes place in small groups where the teacher can closely monitor a child's errors, provide corrective feedback, and otherwise monitor progress and adjust the training. Children do not graduate to more advanced readers until they have demonstrated a measure of competence with more basic readers. In a sense, the teacher is a facilitator who helps children master reading skills.

In contrast, mathematics instruction is frequently done in a large group and practiced alone without direct feedback. However, even among children just beginning school, there are a *wide range of individual differences*. Kindergartners and first-graders are far from uniform in their informal mathematical knowledge and readiness to master formal mathematics (e.g., Baroody, 1987b). With each grade, individual differences become greater.

Because children do not have the same readiness to learn a mathematical concept or skill, a lesson or exercise may not be appropriate for everyone in the class. Thus, new instruction that is introduced to a group of students will probably not be assimilated by all. The problem is compounded when new topics are introduced before a child has had a chance to assimilate more basic lessons. Because new topics often build upon previous lessons, the child gets caught in a downward spiral of failure.

The case of Robert illustrates some of the repercussions of inappropriately paced training.[10] Robert and his parents were very concerned about his ability to keep up with his third-grade class. One day the lad came home and asked if he could stay home from school the next day. Robert had been assigned to learn the nine-times combinations literally overnight and was afraid of the consequences of being unprepared the next day.

Robert's parents checked with his teacher, pointed out that he had not even learned the sixes, sevens, or eights, and the prospect of taking on the nines was overwhelming him. The teacher responded, "You're right, the nines are hard. We'll spend *two days* instead of one day on them!"

Shortly thereafter, Robert's mother asked the interviewer to see her son to determine what was wrong with the boy and if he could be helped. Robert's interview began with a math game (race car) that required players to answer multiplication problems, such as 5 x 3 =?. (The answer determined how many spaces around a race track the player could move his car on his turn.) Robert had no difficulty with combinations involving zero, one, two, fives, or even ten. He had to compute the products of other combinations. He did realize, though, that multiplication was the repeated addition of like terms and that commuted items (e.g., 5 x 3 and 3 x 5) were equivalent.

Robert's pattern of strengths and weaknesses were altogether *typical* of a third-grader. He knew the combinations involving zero and one because of the straightforward rules underlying these "fact families." He also knew the twos, fives, and tens because he was intimately familiar with counting by twos, fives, and tens. Because he saw the connection between multiplication and his existing (skip) count knowledge, he had readily mastered these combinations. He also had a conceptual basis for multiplication: the familiar experience of repeated addition of like terms. Moreover, he had learned that factor order did not affect outcome.

In the case of Robert, the learning problem was not due to deficiencies in his intelligence or character; he was not learning disabled as his mother thought or simply lazy. The problem was created by psychologically inappropriate instruction—the unrealistic expectation that children can master families of arithmetic combinations such as the nine-times facts quickly: in a matter of one or two days.

Learning Deficiencies and Difficulties

When training is conducted in an abstract and lockstep manner, children are forced to memorize mathematics by rote. Some children fail to memorize what seems to be meaningless information correctly or at all and, as a result, learn concepts or procedures in an incomplete or altogether incorrect fashion. Moreover, many children construct beliefs that interfere with further learning and problem-solving efforts.

Mechanical Learning and Thinking

Even when students successfully memorize their lessons and are considered "good students," they may not use their rotely learned knowledge effectively (Davis, 1984). Children frequently fail to see how their formal mathematical knowledge applies to new situations. Consider the case of Ronnie described above. Because he had learned the one-step borrowing procedure by rote and did not understand its underlying rationale, he was unable to reason out how it would apply to somewhat new situations, which required multiple borrowing. A lack of transfer is a common symptom of instruction that is not suited to children's thinking.

Indeed, a steady diet of rote learning can impair self-regulatory capabilities necessary for transfer and problem-solving. That is, it encourages blind rote-following and discourages critical thinking (Holt, 1964). Consider the case of Zelda, a college student taking a mathematics course for elementary teachers.[11] The assignment involved taking squares with sides of 5 cm and cutting each into pieces to make the following shapes: a rectangle, triangle, trapezoid, and parallelogram. For each shape, the student was asked to find its area. Zelda mechanically determined the area for each shape by using a ruler to measure the needed dimensions and plugging the dimensions into the appropriate formula she had memorized. She computed the area of the rectangle, triangle and trapezoid to be 25.0 cm.^{2} Because she mismeasured, she computed the area of the parallelogram as 24.5 cm.^{2} It seemed to make little difference to Zelda that each shape was cut from a square with an area of 25 cm^2 and each had to have the same area.

Bugs

Systematic calculational errors or "bugs" are due to using incorrect or partially correct procedures (e.g., Buswell & Judd, 1925; Brown & Burton, 1978; Ginsburg, 1989), which is especially likely to occur if instruction has little or no meaning to children. In Figure 1, Lymen's subtraction errors[12] were due to a systematic but incorrect procedure: He always subtracted the smaller term from the larger, even when the smaller term was the minuend (top number). Children often use this bug when they have failed to learn the borrowing algorithm in a meaningful manner. Gregory's subtraction bug was the result of not learning a procedure completely. For 40 - 12, for example, the lad realized that he could not subtract 2 from 0. By changing zero to 10, he was able to complete the subtraction of the ones-place digits correctly. Unfortunately, the child did not remember that borrowing from the tens place also involves reducing.

A. Lymen's Incorrect Procedure

52
- 24
32

B. Gregory's Partially Correct Procedure

40
- 12
38

Figure 1 - Example of Student Systematic Errors

Debilitating Beliefs

The way in which mathematics is taught affects how children view mathematics, their learning of the topic, and themselves (Baroody, 1987a). When mathematics is taught in an abstract and lockstep manner, children "hear" such unspoken "messages" as:

- Only geniuses can understand mathematics. It's not something I am supposed to understand or can understand. This is because I'm not very smart.
- Mathematics has nothing to do with me or my world. It's just a bunch of facts and procedures that you have to memorize. What I know or think doesn't matter.
- Arithmetic answers must be given quickly. I have to count. That's because I'm stupid.

Beliefs can have a powerful impact on how children go about learning and using mathematics (Reyes, 1984; Schoenfeld, 1985). For example, because they do not understand their formal instruction and their written assignments do not make sense to them, many children conclude that mathematics is not supposed to make sense. Because of such a belief, they are very likely to stop monitoring their work thoughtfully. This helps to account for the fact that children are not the least bit troubled by answers that are clearly unreasonable. For instance, Lymen, mentioned above in connection with Figure 1, was quite willing to overlook the fact that subtraction cannot yield a difference that is larger than the minuend (the starting amount):

22
- 5
23

Indeed, the feelings and beliefs about mathematics fostered in the primary years can undermine the learning and use of mathematics for years or even a lifetime (Baroody, 1987a). Because they have learned to believe that there is one correct method to solving a problem (the school-taught algorithm), children often respond to problems inflexibly. Indeed, because they have learned to believe that mathematics is foreign to their thinking, they abandon common sense and overlook their own practical knowledge.

Consider what should have been a simple problem-solving exercise. Sherry, a junior high student, explained that her math class was learning how to convert measurements from one unit to another.[13] The interviewer gave Sherry the following problem:

To feed data into the computer, the measurements in your report have to be converted to one unit of measurement: feet. Your first measurement, however, is 3 feet 6 inches. What are you going to feed into the computer?

Sherry recognized immediately that the conversion algorithm taught in school applied: (a) Retrieve the equivalent measures (12 inches = 1 foot); (b) let X = the unknown; (c) set up a proportion (6 inches/12 inches = X/1 foot); (d) cancel units of measure appearing in both the numerator and denominator, (6/12 = X/1 foot); and (e) cross multiply, and simplify the expression (12 times X = 6 times 1 foot ; 12X = 6 feet; 12X/12 = 6 feet/12; X = 0.5 feet). By adding the result of the conversion (0.5 feet) to the whole number of feet (3), it can be determined that 3 feet 6 inches equals 3.5 feet. However, because she really did not understand the rationale behind the conversion algorithm, Sherry had difficulty in remembering the steps and how to execute them. After some time she came up with an improbable answer (it was less than 3 feet). Sherry knew she was in trouble and became flustered. At this point, the interviewer tried to help by asking her if there was any other way of solving the problem. Sherry responded sharply, "No!" She explained, "That's the way it **has** to be done." The interviewer tried to give Sherry a hint: "Look at the numbers in the problem, is there another way we can think about them that might help us figure out the problem more easily?" Sherry grew even more impatient, "This is the way I learned in school, so it has to be the way."

Sherry believed that there was only one way to solve a problem. Though Sherry knew that 6 inches was one half a foot and that the fraction one-half was equivalent to the decimal expression .5, she did not use this knowledge to solve the problem informally and quickly ("3 feet-6 inches is 3 1/2 or 3.5 feet). Her beliefs prevented her from effectively using her existing mathematical knowledge to solve the problem (Schoenfeld, 1985).

Conclusions

Cognitive research indicates that it is essential to distinguish between meaningful learning and rote learning (e.g., Resnick & Ford, 1981). It is not enough to absorb and accumulate information. Children must be given the opportunity to assimilate mathematical knowledge—to construct accurate and complete mathematical understandings. This requires that instruction build upon children's existing knowledge, which for primary children is their counting-based informal mathematical knowledge. Such an approach is important for fostering self-regulation and a positive disposition toward mathematical learning and problem solving—as well as meaningful learning.

Notes

1. The case of Alison was compiled by the first author.

2. Her mental addition was also limited in terms of the size of the addend as well as the sum. She could not add on more than two accurately (e.g., six and three more).

3. Alison's counting performance also appeared to exhibit strength and weakness. Despite the fact that she did not know the correct sequence beyond 11, she consistently said the nonstandard terms (as well as the terms 1 to 11) in the same order. This is consistent with the view that her counting behavior was guided by a "stable-order principle" (e.g., Gelman & Gallistel, 1978).

4. Sarita was interviewed by the second author.

5. Mike was interviewed by Cathy A. Mason. The case study was originally reported in Baroody (1987a).

6. The case of Aaron is reprinted here from Baroody (1987a), with the permission of Teachers College Press.

7. The interview with Raul was conducted by the second author.

8. Arianne was interviewed by the first author.

9. The interview with Ronnie was conducted by the first author.

10. Robert was interviewed by the first author.

11. The case of Zelda was noted by Marta Civil, a doctoral student in the College of Education at the University of Illinois at Urbana-Champaign.

12. The data on Lymen and Gregory were collected with the help of Dr. Barbara S. Allardice, now the mathematics coordinator of the Learning Development Center at the Rochester Institute of Technology.

13. The interview with Sherry was conducted by the first author.

Chapter 5: What Do We Do When We "Do Mathematics"?

Robert B. Davis and Carolyn A. Maher
Rutgers University

"Every theory," Albert Einstein once said, "should be as simple as possible, but no simpler." We argue here that those of us who study the learning and teaching of mathematics are handicapped by encounters with theories that *are*, indeed, simpler than the allowable minimum. The antidote, we argue, consists of two necessary steps: careful observation of the *details* of people who are dealing with mathematical situations of various sorts, and the postulation of somewhat more elaborated theories.

We state, first, a piece of an "elaborated" theory, taken from Davis (1984). The central piece of this theory is, essentially, the following: In order to think about a mathematical situation, one must cycle (perhaps many times) through these steps:

1. Build a representation for the input data.
2. From this *data* representation, carry out memory searches to retrieve or construct a representation of (hopefully) relevant knowledge that can be used in solving the problem or otherwise going further with the task.
3. Construct a mapping between the *data* representation and the *knowledge* representation.
4. Check this mapping (and these constructions) to see if they seem to be correct.
5. When the constructions and the mapping appear satisfactory, use technical devices (or other information) associated with the knowledge representation in order to solve the problem.

One could add more "surface" details to this outline (such as "checking the final results"), but these are not fundamental to the processes of human thought (even though they can be valuable!) in the same way that our basic steps are.

What Do These Terms Mean?

In Step 1 we speak of a "representation." In general we mean primarily a *mental representation,* although it often happens that one makes use of paper and pencil, or even of physical materials, to help out in the process of building an adequate representation. If I say the word "dog," you surely have some sort of mental representation of the meaning of that word. For those of us who try to study how humans *think* about mathematics, it is perhaps unfortunate that this building of representations usually occurs so quickly and effortlessly that we are inclined to doubt that anything at all has happened. As is often the case, this process is most conspicuous when it is absent. In contrast to the situation with "dog," if I say "oquassa" you probably do *not* have any mental image to represent the meaning of the word. For many students, the same would be true of "square root" or of "exponential rate of growth." This building of representations is by no means a trivial matter, nor is it merely a question of knowing the meanings of the words in the familiar sense. Consider the task of building a representation for a chess board with eight queens on it, so placed that no queen is under attack from any other. It may be easy for most of us to build a representation for "three dimes, to which we add two more dimes," but can you build a representation for "a trash can containing 736 pieces of trash, to which are added an additional 1,987 pieces of trash"? If the trash can contains yesterdays New York Times, does that count as *one* piece of trash, or should we separate the pages and hence count it as perhaps 14 pieces? Was there a cookie among those original 736 pieces? If so, did the addition of 1,987 *more* pieces cause the cookie to crumble? If it did, how many pieces does the cookie now consist of?

In a moment we will look at this process of building a "representation for the input data" in the case of Brian, a fifth grade boy whose actions and words were recorded on videotape and subsequently carefully analyzed.

In Step 2 we speak of "building a representation of (possibly) relevant knowledge." This, too, is a process that may take place so quickly that we fail to notice that it exists at all. Consider the problem: "Mary had three dolls. For Christmas she received two more. How many dolls does Mary have now?" Adults reading this paragraph may see this almost immediately as "a problem in addition." Yet in fact, two separate steps are involved: first we need a representation of the *situation;* then we need a representation of "possibly relevant knowledge." For a child, the second may not spring immediately (nor effortlessly) from the first. Consider a different problem: "Mary has three blouses and two skirts. How many different combinations can she make?" In this problem, getting from a data representation to a representation of possibly helpful knowledge may not be so automatic at all. Or consider this problem: "We are going to write down strings of zeros and ones. One example might be:

01001011

If we agree that every string that we write must be exactly 8 digits long, how many different strings can we write?" Here, too, the process of getting from a representation of the input data—what is the problem or situation?—to a representation of possibly useful knowledge may not be trivial for many people.

We want to emphasize that our purpose is not merely to construct a theory of how people think about elementary school mathematics; we want to deal also with mathematics at any level whatsoever. If we make little use of examples such as "Describe the Quik Sort algorithm using pseudocode," it is because we feel that such examples might have less value for many readers, not because we believe that the basic ways of thinking about mathematics are different at more advanced levels (although obstacles and demands vary as one moves into other levels and topics).

Step 3 is "constructing a mapping between the data representation and the knowledge representation." An example may make this notion clearer. It has recently been announced that, for Christmas, 1989, a major US corporation will give five cents to charity for every letter written to Santa Claus (at the official US Post Office "Santa Claus" address), up to the first two million letters. What is the most that this offer may cost the company in actual contributed dollars (there may be other processing costs that we disregard)?

A mathematics teacher reports that he solved this problem as follows: First, he assumed the maximum number of letters, two million. Then he reasoned: "Well, that would cost the company two million dollars, *if* they were offering one dollar per letter. But they aren't; they are offering five cents per letter. So, that's one twentieth of a dollar. Therefore we want to divide 2,000,000 by 20. OK—let's divide 2,000,000 by 2 (He was doing all of this in his head, without recourse to paper and pencil, nor to calculator.). That's one million. Now I still have to divide by 10. So the most the offer could cost is $100,000."

Without looking at every detail, there were several points in his reasoning where he made mappings between representations. One time, for example, when he replaced "one nickel" by the idea of "dividing by twenty." He reported that he was aware of checking this mapping by asking himself if it was correct that there are 20 nickels in a dollar. We might analyze his thought process by saying that, after constructing some representation for the input data, he quickly made up a representation for "relevant knowledge" [1], a representation that he knew in advance would be wrong, but that he hoped would be useful—he imagined a contribution of two million dollars. But his checking revealed, as he knew it would, that this was incorrect, and that he could not map the problem data into this representation—it would imply a contribution of $1 per letter. So he rejected this representation—or, more accurately, he began immediately to modify it. He must reduce the amount to reflect a payment of 5 cents per letter, not one dollar.

The theory we present here is by no means a finished theory. In the present example, for instance, one could well argue about the sequential order in which events took place. Is it, in fact, correct to speak of a second representation, with a mapping between the two? Or would it be more accurate to speak of one representation, the initial "letter" representation, which is thereafter transformed, indeed through an extended sequence of transformations?[2]

We see no immediate way to settle such questions, nor even to assess how important such distinctions may be. (As Kurt Lewin once remarked, "Differences that do not make differences are not differences!") But we do argue that a postulated theory that *attempts* to deal with the question of mental representations may serve us better than one that ignores their very existence.

It should be emphasized that in most cases one must cycle through the steps (or through some of them, at least) many times before getting a "final" result. Except for problems of the greatest simplicity, it rarely happens that one can move through the complete sequence of steps only once and come directly to a final answer. In particular, most of the subjects whom we have observed do not "take in" a complete problem statement at the beginning. The "data representation," their mental version of the problem statement, apparently must be built up gradually, in stages.

Brian and the Two-Pizza Problem

The time has come to look in more detail at some actual human behavior. The data we will now discuss comes from a videotape recording made in a fifth grade classroom in a public school in a blue-collar working class area in New Jersey. The class was working, as it commonly did, in small groups; each group consisted of two or three children. A television camera was aimed at a group consisting of two boys, Brian and Scott. No adult was involved in this episode; the teacher herself was working elsewhere in the classroom at the time of the episode which we discuss.

(Our data are taken from an unpublished doctoral dissertation by J. Landis [1990]; the analysis presented here is new.) The class had been asked to solve the following problem:

> *At Pizza Hut each large pizza is cut into 12 slices. Mrs. Elson ordered two large pizzas. Seven students from Mrs. Elson's class are to eat one piece from each of the pizzas. What fraction of the two pizzas was eaten?*

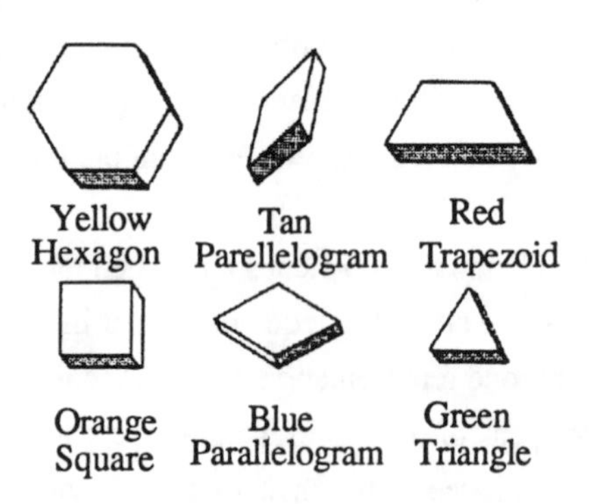

Figure 1 - Pattern Blocks

Brian and Scott had, available on their table, a variety of manipulatable materials that they could use if they wished. In the present episode they used "Pattern Blocks," wooden blocks shaped as shown in Figure 1. The dimensions and shapes of the blocks are so arranged that six of the green triangles fit on top of one of the yellow hexagons. Alternatively, two of the red trapezoids fit on the yellow hexagon. One blue parallelogram can combine with one green triangle to cover exactly the red trapezoid. (The reader can work out other arrangements that will fit exactly.) The tan parallelogram and the orange square are exceptions to this "commensurability," and do not fit onto anything else. There are many blocks of each kind available in the pile on the table.

Brian: [Reads the problem aloud, then picks up one of the blocks, a yellow hexagon] This is one pizza.

Brian is trying to make a representation of the information given in the problem (or, more accurately, of **that part** *of the data that deals with the pizza; he as not yet gotten to the matter of representing the students who eat the pizza).*

Brian: [Picks up several smaller pieces, apparently intending to indicate slices] No, *this* is one pizza [as he puts down *two* yellow hexagons].

Notice what he has done: His checking of his representation showed him that he would not be able to find twelfths. So he has taken a step of breathtaking subtlety: He uses two pieces of wood (carefully chosen) to represent one pizza.

Brian: This is a pizza, here. [He is merely restating his new definition, presumably for the benefit of Scott, his partner.]

Scott: Yeah. [He, too, picks up two hexagons.] These are the two pizzas.

Notice that Scott has missed the subtlety of Brian's representation of ***one*** *pizza by two hexagons. Scott is using* ***one*** *hexagon to represent* ***one*** *pizza. Our observations show us, time and time again, that a very difficult step, often taken incorrectly, is matching your mental representation to* ***someone else's.*** *In the present case, Scott has not correctly matched his representation to Brian's.*

At this point there is some rather inconclusive mumbling back and forth; each boy is mainly thinking about his own work, and trying not to be distracted by the other.

Brian: OK [His posture and tone make it clear that he is not really responding to Scott; in fact he is really ignoring Scott.]

Scott: Yeah, this is one pizza.

It is possible that Scott has now adopted Brian's representation, and is using two hexagons to represent one pizza, but this is not entirely certain. The videotape does not provide conclusive evidence either way.

Brian: [Who has been fitting small green triangles, representing *slices,* on top of a hexagon] This [picking up a red trapezoid] counts as three greens, OK? [Brian is still ignoring Scott and carrying through his own solution of the problem. Brian apparently wants to use the red trapezoid so as to have fewer pieces of wood to handle.]

Scott: Wait! I just figured it out! If you have twelve pieces and you have seven students getting a piece ... wait! ... chopped into twelve slices [virtually talking to himself at this point] ... each of the students getting one piece of these twelve ... There's seven students, right? So, for two pizzas that would be fourteen slices of this. ... Brian, if you added it all together, and then you have eight slices left over

Brian: Just think about it.

Brian's tone seems to say either "Don't bother me, can't you see I'm busy?" or else, perhaps, Brian has realized that Scott's representation is wrong, and is asking him to reconsider it. In either case, Brian doesn't want to be interrupted in his own thought processes, as his manner makes very clear.

Scott: You have eight left over. ...

Brian: Keep thinking about it. [i.e., "Don't bother me right now!"] So ... nineteen and nineteen is ...

Scott: Thirty six.

Brian: Thirty eight.

This (and, indeed, the tape in general) shows how these two boys can have several "layers" or "levels" of conversation [and, presumably, thought] going on essentially simultaneously. We have not tried to analyze this phenomenon, but someone surely should, sooner or later. At one level, Scott has used a representation irreconcilable with Brian's; this may still be bothering Brian, and a few remarks may refer to this ("Think about it!"). At another level Brian seems to be saying to Scott something like "I'm really busy on some hard calculations right now; please don't interrupt."[3] But when Brian himself thinks aloud ("Nineteen and nineteen is ..."), Scott answers him (incorrectly): "Thirty six." Brian notices Scott's error in arithmetic, and corrects Scott: "Thirty-eight." And, of course, during all of this, Brian is mainly engaged in building up a mental representation for the data in the original problem about children eating slices from two pizzas.

Brian: But there's only twenty-four slices!

Scott: How do you figure "twenty-four" slices? This is a pizza, Brian! This is twelve slices. [He shows two hexagons, so at this point he seems to have adopted Brian's representation.] This is one pizza.

Brian: Twelve [displaying two hexagons]. Twenty-four [puts down two more hexagons, for a combined array of four hexagons].

Brian: [changing the subject] OK ... how many boys are in the class?

Actually, Brian is now beginning to work on building another part of the data representation, the representation of the children who are to eat the pizza. He has not recalled correctly the statement of the problem. Here, too, we see many "layers" - Brian probably built up a preliminary "primitive" representation of the problem in which the idea of "children in a class" was not well represented, and he has managed to confuse this idea with the idea of "boys in my own class right now".

Scott: One, two, three, four, five, six, ... I think eight.

Brian: [repeating himself] How many boys are in the class?

Scott: What class?

Here, too, we see an indication of the many layers of thinking that seem to go on simultaneously. The first time that Brian asked this question, Scott merely counted the boys he could see. Brian seems somehow not to have heard (or not to have believed) Scott, and asked the same question again. But the repetition seems to have pushed Scott down to a deeper layer of thought, and he has begun to wonder why Brian has asked the same question again. Scott now wonders whether they are both talking about the same class, so he asks about this.[4]

Brian: Our class.

Scott: Why do you want to know about the number of boys?

Brian: Just count them!

Scott: Nineteen, all together. There's 6, ... thirteen boys.

Brian: Thirteen and thirteen, that's twenty six.

Scott: Briiiaaaan......

Brian: Here's the pizzas. [He has in place four yellow hexagons, two for each "pizza," and he is beginning to cover them with small green triangles, representing slices.]

Scott: Brian. ... Brian! Figure this, Brian!

Brian: I think I know it.

Scott: I already figured it out. You wouldn't want to do it, Brian.

While Brian has been trying to build a representation using the Pattern Blocks, Scott has been trying to work the problem out on paper. Scott's words, here, seem to mean: "You wouldn't want to solve this problem by working it out on paper, Brian!" It subsequently turns out that Scott's paper-and-pencil "solution" is in fact incorrect.

Brian: [Still working with the Pattern Blocks] Yes, I would! Get me two greens [from that pile] over there.

Scott: Sure, if you feel like doing the work, OK.

Brian: OK, what's the answer?

Having now almost completed his construction with the blocks, Brian is really mainly talking to himself, here. In effect he is saying: "OK. Now I see what the problem is. If I look at this right, can I see the answer?"

Scott: You have to listennnn.

Brian: So ... There's *one* pizza ... [Two hexagons, now covered with small green triangles to show twelve "slices."]

Scott: I'm gonna listen to your solution right now and then you're gonna listen to mine.

Brian: [who is still working on his concrete representation of the pizzas, using Pattern Blocks] Get me twelve more of those [referring to the small green triangles].

Scott: Here you go.

Brian: 1 ... 3, 4, 6, 8, 10, 12 ... Thank you. ... and ... here is *another* pizza!

Scott: Now keep in mind that you were wrong last time.

Further evidence of the many different levels on which the children are thinking, more or less simultaneously.

Brian: Keep in mind that I was right more times than you!

Scott: That's why you got the whole ditto wrong, and I got the whole ditto right! I had it right!

Brian: I wouldn't do it your way.

Presumably Brian is rejecting the paper-and-pencil calculation that Scott has completed.

Scott: OK. ... I want to watch your solution and see if it's the same as mine.

Brian has carefully assembled two shapes, each of which consists of two hexagons built from small green triangles. He has thus modeled the two pizzas, with twelve slices on each of them. It is important to notice that he has ***not*** *yet started to model the* ***children eating*** *the two pizzas.*

Brian: I might be wrong.

Scott: No, I'm not saying that you're wrong. I want to see if it's the same as mine.

Brian: Here's the two pizzas [gestures toward the four hexagons]. Now, everybody gets a slice out of *this* pizza [pointing to the first pair of hexagons]. OK?

Scott: Not *everybody!* Only ... [Scott picks up the paper and starts to reread the statement of the problem .[5] Seven students from Mrs. Elson's class are to eat one slice from each of the two pizzas.

Brian: So ... seven ...

And here Brian does something truly stunning; as he works to model the next part of the problem—namely, the students eating the slices—he is just as concrete as he was in using the Pattern Blocks to model the pizzas themselves.

Brian [He looks around the class, and points to individual students, naming the specific student who is to eat each slice] So this [pushing one "slice" toward Scott, and one toward himself] is for you and for me; Ron [pointing to a student], Rav [pointing to another student], Jennifer [again pointing], Mary [pointing to Mary], and Melissa [pointing to Melissa]. [As he names each child, he moves one slice" away from the *second* "pizza"]. [Rereading the problem] What fraction of the two pizzas was eaten? Two, four, six, eight, ten, twelve, fourteen. So ... 24 out of 14.[6] I mean, 14 out of 24. [He writes the fraction 14/24.]

Scott: No! You can't change that bottom number! You can't change the 12. It's 14/12. [By "bottom number" Scott of course means the denominator, which Brian has just written as "24."]

From watching Scott and Brian throughout the videotaped session, it is clear that Scott is oriented toward trying to solve these problems by paper-and-pencil methods, whereas Brian usually prefers to make concrete representations using the Pattern Blocks. It is also clear that Scott's solutions are often wrong, and that Brian usually ***understands*** *the problems better (presumably as a result of his care in making representations of the problem data).* [7]

The preceding excerpt from a videotaped session shows very clearly how a student may go about building up a representation for the "input data" from some problem statement or situation. It is particularly valuable for the way it shows the student breaking the representation-building task into parts: first he constructs a representation for the **pizzas**, ignoring the children who will eat them; then, when that construction has been completed, he builds a representation for the **eaters**, ignoring (for the moment) the pizzas. This is typical of the behavior we find, both in students and in adult experts; people rarely try to take in an entire problem, but work instead to build representations for various separate pieces.

If a student had to choose between a paper-and-pencil solution of a problem, and one where the answer was obtained more directly from a concrete representation, which would they choose? We have many taped interviews that bear on this question; in the next section we look at one of them.

Ling Chen and the Candy Bar Problem

Ling Chen, a Chinese girl in an urban school, had just completed the fifth grade. During the summer she was in a special program for gifted students, where she was interviewed by Regina Lemerich. The interview was recorded on videotape; the data we use here come from a study of the tape, presented in Maher and Alston (1989). The following problem was given to Ling:

Jane has one third of a candy bar. She gives half of what she has to Mike. How much of a candy bar does she give to Mike?

Ling Chen has available to her, on the table, a large variety of manipulatable materials, including the same kind of Pattern Blocks that Brian used in our previous example. In fact, it is these same blocks that Ling Chen chooses to use in making a representation of the problem here.

Teacher: Use anything here to figure it out.

Ling builds a model of the problem with the Pattern Blocks, and makes a picture of her work on paper. We show the final form of her paper in Figure 2. To begin, Ling selects the yellow hexagon to represent the candy bar; this allows her to use one blue parallelogram to represent "one third of a candy bar," which is Jane's initial share.

Ling: This [pointing to the blue parallelogram] is one third of a candy bar. See, she gives one half to Mike. This is Mike's [pointing to a small green triangle]. One half of one third is one sixth.

Teacher: So! What's your answer?

Ling: One sixth.

Teacher: Can you write it down?

Ling writes the fraction correctly. At this point she also labels her drawing of the Pattern Block solution (see Figure 2).

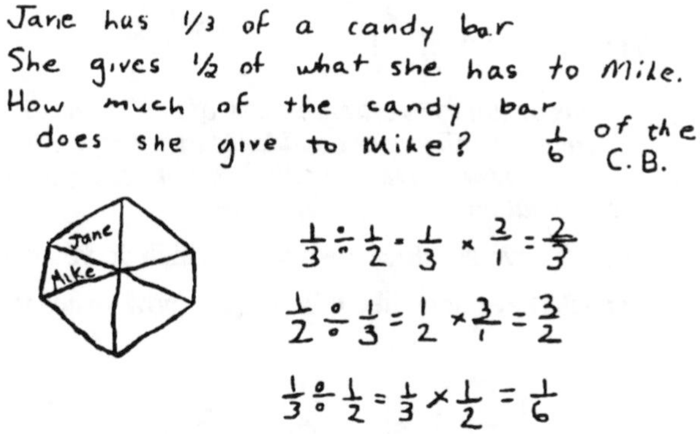

Jane has 1/3 of a candy bar
She gives ½ of what she has to Mike.
How much of the candy bar
does she give to Mike? $\frac{1}{6}$ of the C. B.

Jane
Mike

$\frac{1}{3} \div \frac{1}{2} = \frac{1}{3} \times \frac{2}{1} = \frac{2}{3}$

$\frac{1}{2} \div \frac{1}{3} = \frac{1}{2} \times \frac{3}{1} = \frac{3}{2}$

$\frac{1}{3} \div \frac{1}{2} = \frac{1}{3} \times \frac{1}{2} = \frac{1}{6}$

Figure 2 - Ling's Drawing

Ling: See! One sixth! Six of these [the small green triangles] make the candy bar [represented by the hexagon].

Teacher: Can you do this one with numbers?
[Ling works at this for some time, producing first the line shown below]

$$\frac{1}{3} \div \frac{1}{2} = \frac{1}{3} \times \frac{2}{1} = \frac{2}{3}$$

This is a stunning example of one of the phenomena we are concerned about: Ling is clearly a good student; she has learned the "invert and multiply" rule correctly. But she has produced an incorrect answer! How come? Because she has not called upon the correct algorithmic solution procedure. There is no reliable way to go from a problem statement to a solution procedure unless you get a correct representation of the problem. Of course, Ling has before her both the "algorithmic solution" and a correct representation. Given these two stimuli, how will she react?

Teacher: Which answer do you believe [that is, the answer one-sixth, obtained directly from the problem representation, or the answer two-thirds, obtained from using the "invert and multiply" algorithm]?

Ling: I believe it's one-sixth. ... [pause] ... Maybe I did ... [pause] ... I should have done it like this ... [pause] ... She now writes the next line on her paper:

$$\frac{1}{2} \div \frac{1}{3} = \frac{1}{2} \times \frac{3}{1} = \frac{3}{2}$$

Ling: That's not right either!

She has begun to question her use of the "invert and multiply" rule, apparently having more confidence in her representation solution. But even with this change, she still does not get a match with the representation answer of one-sixth.

Teacher: Now you've got *three* answers! Which do you believe?

Ling: I should have done like this ... [She now writes the line below.]

$$\frac{1}{3} \div \frac{1}{2} = \frac{1}{3} \times \frac{1}{2} = \frac{1}{6}$$

This gives us a measure of her desperation. She has come to the point of claiming that one-third ***divided by*** *one-half is the same thing as one-third* ***times*** *one-half, something she can hardly believe if these processes have any real meaning for her. But some pay-off has appeared; she has finally carried out a paper-and-pencil calculation that has produced the same answer that she obtained from using her concrete representation!*

Teacher: Circle the part that you think is right.
[Unfortunately, Ling never does this (see Figure 2).]

Ling: I should have multiplied these numbers because these two numbers add ... [pause] ... no ... [pause] ... whatever! ... [pause] ... *go together* to make one-sixth.

So—Ling is in fact sure of the answer, but has difficulty making any of her algorithmic work produce the answer she believes is correct. At the time of this interview, it is clear that concrete representations work far better for her than the algorithms do.

We do not argue against teaching algorithms. (Indeed, within this chapter we do not argue for or against anything in the area of *teaching*. Our present concern is with the way children think. But, see Chapter 6 for ideas about teaching.) However, for theoretical reasons we believe that it is difficult, if not impossible, to go directly from the statement of a problem to the construction of a correct algorithmic approach, and we think that our data show this very clearly indeed.

Summary

First, our purpose in this chapter is to take a look at the **very complicated** things that human beings do when they think about mathematics. We work with rather minutely-detailed videotaped examples of behavior, and we relate this data to a theory, taken from Davis (1984), that gives it structure.

However, even with this goal in mind, it is impossible to study these episodes without suspecting that mathematics teaching could be considerably improved if teachers made more use of having students engage in the *explicit* construction of concrete representations of problem "input" data.

One could go much further. When you put these excerpts of actual student behavior up against the typical K-12 mathematics curriculum, it becomes immediately evident that, except for tenth-grade Euclidean geometry, the curriculum deals *only* with memorized algorithmic procedures. Real mathematics does not consist mainly of algorithms, however. Mathematicians *analyze problems* and *create* algorithms, they do not merely memorize algorithms and recall them as needed. These studies show that children do exactly the same creative sorts of things that mathematicians do. The curriculum, however, discourages this, and in the process all too often discourages the children themselves.

Notes

1. Although the teacher did not report any "smaller" steps than this, it seems nearly certain that there must have been some—indeed, there must have been many. He could hardly have arrived instantaneously at the idea of asking how *many nickels there are in a dollar*. He must have made some simple representations of the problem situation (and apparently also of "relevant knowledge") so that, by some sort of "bootstrapping," he was able to get to larger organized pieces of knowledge. It is quite typical that we are aware only of the larger pieces, and not of the smaller bootstrapping steps that led to them.

2. If the teacher was in fact able to report his thought processes with enough accuracy, then we are seeing a method of solving problems by what we might call "successive modifications." His first knowledge representation (the "$2, 000, 000") was made in the full realization that it would be wrong, and with the expectation that it might be changed into something better. We have other interviews with this same subject, and the creation of a sequence of representations by the successive modification of each one in order to arrive at the next one was a method that he used quite routinely. It seemed almost to be his preferred method of problem solving (see also Davis, 1985a). It is, of course, a very familiar method for all of us. How is one usually taught, in traditional ninth-grade algebra courses, to solve equations such as the following:

$$3x + 7 - 2x + 9 = 12 - 2x + 10 \ ?$$

By changing the (written) representation one step at a time, until one arrives at an equation (in this case, $x = 2$) for which the solution is obvious. Unfortunately, the power and generality of this method—or even its description as a sequential modification of representations—are usually *not* taught.

3. When we say Brian was busy with a "calculation" we probably misspeak. We think it would be more accurate to say that Brian was busy *building up his representation of the problem situation*. Our observations for several years have suggested that *building mental representations* (and most of Brian's representation is "in his mind," not lying in pieces on the table) *is extremely difficult*. Whenever we are doing it we dislike interruptions. (See, e.g., Davis, 1987b, pages 110-111.)

4. Our analysis of this videotape is probably influenced by our study of the very important manuscript by Schoenfeld, Smith & Arcavi (in press). Our analysis is not as detailed as theirs, but we see the merit of paying very close attention to what can be picked up on a single videotape. (See also Landis and Maher, 1989.)

5. This is entirely typical of the way we find students gradually building up their representations of problems. In our studies we rarely find a student taking in the entire meaning of a problem on his or her first reading of it. Nearly always they must cycle back and build up a problem representation by successive approximations.

6. Here is another instance of an incorrect mapping. Brian has the schema "X out of Y," but he incorrectly maps "24" into X and "14" into Y. Fortunately, Brian is one of those people who usually checks his mappings carefully, so he catches the error at once, and immediately corrects it.

7. In this analysis our fundamental concern is how children think; it is *not* (within the present chapter) mainly a concern for teaching. Nonetheless, there is a question that will surely arise in the minds of some readers: Is Brian becoming too tied to concrete approaches that can only succeed when small numbers are involved? This goes beyond the kind of observed data that this chapter deals with, but the question does perhaps deserve some kind of answer. First, the most important observation may be that Brian's *understanding* does lead him to correct answers, whereas Scott's efforts to work with symbols that he does *not* understand lead him to incorrect answers. This is probably a case where "correct" is really better! Second, we believe that Brian is *not* being limited by what he is doing. Indeed, tapes of Brian, made one year later, do not show such limitations. Brian has become quite good at using symbols in the usual ways. The only difference might be that he typically does it correctly! Finally, even if large numbers were involved, Brian's "concrete" methods would still be applicable; one would merely have to choose meanings correctly. Indeed, Brian does this already in the present session, when he uses one red trapezoid to represent three small green triangles. To pursue this further would take us away from our present theme, how humans think about mathematics. We do strongly argue, though, that this has important implications for curriculum and for pedagogy!

Chapter 6: Building Representations of Children's Meanings

Carolyn A. Maher and Robert B . Davis
Rutgers University

In Chapter 5 (Davis & Maher, this volume) we suggested the importance of paying attention to the fine detail of children's ideas. We have given instances of videotaped episodes of children engaged in thinking about mathematics as they worked to construct a solution to a problem. An analysis of the children's mathematical behavior has given us some insight into how they built up their representation of the problem. We have observed their attempts to connect this mental representation to the physical model that they also built, the picture that they drew, and their written symbolic statement of the problem situation. Having looked at *children* in Chapter 5, in the present chapter we shall look at how difficult is the *teacher's* task of recognizing the actual ideas of students.

Background

We consider in this chapter a classroom episode in which a teacher's representation of a problem situation is in conflict with that of her student's, Brian. The teacher, a second-year participant in a teacher development project in mathematics, was attempting to implement her growing knowledge of content, children's learning, and pedagogy in her classroom (Maher & Alston,1988). She began to include small cooperative group problem-solving explorations as a regular classroom activity, and she was integrating in her lessons problem tasks in which children were encouraged to build physical models to represent their solutions. The Brian and Scott episode described and analyzed in Chapter 5 was representative of her instruction at this stage of her participation in the project.

The two fifth-grade students whom we saw in Chapter 5, Brian and Scott, worked together regularly as partners doing mathematics. Having considered the work and thought processes of these two students in the previous chapter, we now attempt to see their thinking from the perspective of their teacher. In fact, because we have the advantage of videotapes of Brian and Scott working together in earlier lessons, and we also have the notes written by the teacher after each of these lessons, we are able to study their thinking in close detail. From this we can gain added insight into their mathematical thinking precisely because we can watch it *develop*. (Of course, we also have the advantage of hindsight, and the opportunity to look at tapes over and over again, discuss them, look some more, discuss some more, and so on. This is very different from the situation that confronted the teacher when she was actually teaching the class, and had to respond in "real time." The result is that we, today, can know far more about Brian and Scott than the teacher could when she was teaching the lesson.)

In these earlier lessons, we see Brian trying to solve some fraction problems by drawing pictures, looking at what he has drawn, and describing what he sees—but he describes what he sees in a way that does not match the problem he is supposed to be solving.

Consider this example: one problem, as actually posed, had been: "Eight children are given one-fourth of a candy bar apiece. How much candy is that altogether?" Brian had attempted to solve the problem by drawing quarters which he arranged to be essentially two rectangles, each partitioned into four blocks, not at all a bad rendering of the candy bar situation in the problem. But at this point Brian gets into trouble. He looks at what he has drawn and says that this represents "eight eighths" (see Figure 1). The picture certainly showed eight *pieces*, so in that sense Brian's description contained some truth, but it clearly was unlikely to lead him to a correct solution of the problem. All of this had happened earlier, before the episode discussed in Chapter 5.

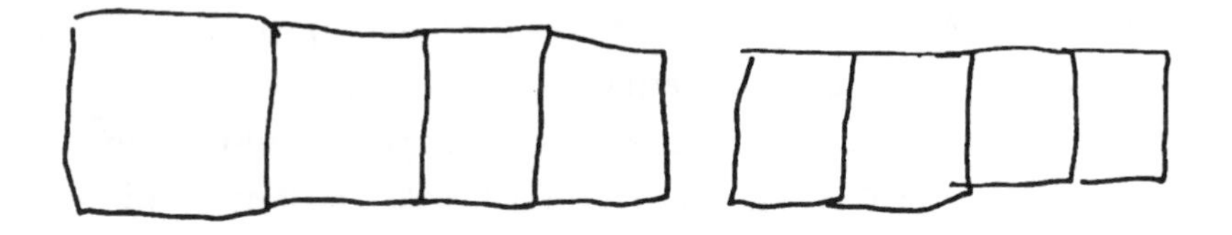

Figure 1 - Brian's Drawing

If we follow along in the videotaped record from one day to the next we arrive finally at the Chapter 5 episode of Brian and Scott. If we keep watching, we can see the teacher, who has been circulating around the classroom, finally come to the desk where the two boys are working. We now see her trying to make sense of what the boys have been doing. She observes that her own representation of the problem situation does not match that of Brian. The teacher believes her own solution is correct (in fact, it is not). Consequently, she feels that she must help Brian (who actually is correct) to see his error. We now extend our study of the problem-solving behavior of Brian and Scott, focusing this time on the interaction of the teacher with these two students.

A Classroom Episode

In the critical episode, the problem that Brian and Scott have been working is:

At Pizza Hut each large pizza is cut into 12 slices. Mrs. Elson ordered two large pizzas. Seven students from Mrs. Elson's class are to eat one piece from each of the pizzas. What fraction of the two pizzas was eaten?

Brian made a concrete representation of the problem, and Scott tried to solve the problem using paper-and-pencil procedures. Brian's solution (which was correct) was reflected by the representation that he built while Scott's solution (which was incorrect) was an outcome of his search for some rule or procedure that he might apply to solve the problem. Scott's search to find a procedure or rule to the problem situation seemed to dominate the way he thought about doing the problem to the extent that he found it difficult to listen to Brian's interpretation of the problem data. In a parallel way, Brian was so engrossed in building a representation of the problem situation that he seemed to dismiss Scott's interruptions. The videotape shows clearly that Scott and Brian have not been able to build mental representations that can be related to one another.

Brian's problem-solving activity showed his ability to make a connection among several schema that he constructed and connected as he built a solution to the problem. He began by using Pattern Blocks to make some concrete representations of the pizzas (yellow hexagons and green triangles; also, red trapezoids and green triangles). He related the model(s) he built to a representation of students who would eat the pizza. He was then able to describe his answer using numbers that appeared to make sense to him.

Teacher-Student Mental Representation Conflict

Recall that while the Brian and Scott problem-solving session was taking place, the teacher had been circulating from group to group. She had not been present when Brian and Scott were working on the problem. Just as the two boys finished, the teacher came to their table. The videotape continues to run, and shows us what happened when the teacher turned her attention to Brian and Scott and tried to figure out what they had been doing. The following episode begins with Brian explaining his solution to the teacher (with Scott occasionally joining in).

Brian: Here ...

Teacher: Do you, uh ...

Scott: I think we got it right.

Brian: I think I know I'm right.

Scott: Yeah, we think we know we're right.

Brian: So there's 24 slices in both pizzas, so Mrs. E. wants 7 students ... she took 7 students to Pizza Hut, so...she's gonna give 'em one slice from each pizza so we would have , uh, 14 out of the 24, right, slices.

Teacher: All right, now let me ask you this. How do you get 24 slices in the one pizza, and 12 slices in the other?
Note that this is not what Brian had actually done or said. See the complete transcript of this episode in Chapter 5 .

Earlier observations. Related to the preceding episode is an important event that occurred in a previous lesson:

Teacher: You had 3/8 of this pizza and 3/8 of that pizza. How much is that?

Brian: 6/16.

Teacher: But the pizza has only 8 pieces.

Scott: Is this right? 6/8?

Teacher: Why isn't it 16ths?

Scott: Because the pizza has 8 pieces and you can't change it.

In the teacher's comment to this lesson, she wrote:

> As I circulated the room, I saw students continued to have problems with mixed nos. & reducing. Some students continue to add denominators. Brian continues to add the denominators.

Her notes reveal that the teacher, like a great many people, tended to think of "arithmetic" in terms of the manipulation of symbols. Consequently, she interprets Brian's behavior as "adding denominators." But we have had the advantage of watching him build representations of the problem that are, in fact, good replicas of the actual meaning.

One might also wish that the teacher had wondered more about the commonness of the "adding denominators" behavior. This might have led her to think further about why so many different children were coming up with similar interpretations. But all of us who have taught know how quickly a classroom situation develops, allowing teachers no time for reflection. One must act quickly, and without the benefit of videotaped "instant replays."

Teacher-Student Interaction

We might describe this situation by saying that one of the tasks that a teacher faces is to construct in her or his own mind a mental representation that matches the student's mental representation. What might be some consequences in the short and long run if the teacher's representation mismatches that of the student?

Let us return to the episode of the teacher's intervention with Brian and Scott when Brian had *14 out of 24* and the teacher objected. The teacher's tone might be described here as slightly disapproving and surprised. She was anticipating that **one pizza** consisting of **twelve slices** would serve as the unit (Her lesson plan, planning notes, comments after reviewing the video tape of this episode, and subsequent discussion about the problem indicate that this was her interpretation).

Brian: In all.

Teacher: Brian

Brian: There's 12 slices in the one pizza, and 12 slices in the other.

At this point the teacher interrupted Brian and told him how he (they) should think about the pizzas. Scott smiled, nodded victoriously, indicating satisfaction to Brian that his solution seemed to be vindicated.

Teacher: All right, we should think of them as 2 separate pizzas, though, right? [Scott nods affirmatively]

Brian now seemed ready to abandon his solution. The teacher directed the students by correcting their work; she discarded Brian's solution (which had, in fact, been correct) by mentioning that there was no box big enough for such a "gi-huge-ic" pizza. Brian again tried to justify how this might be done but is interrupted by the teacher before he is heard.

Brian: Yeah ...

Teacher: OK, you, you're putting your 2 pizzas together and making one ... gi-huge-ic pizza.

Scott: [laughing] Gi-huge-ic pizza

Teacher: OK, we can't have one gi-huge-ic pizza because there isn't a box that could carry it in to take it home. (*Note that this is completely irrelevant to the problem.*)

Brian: No, just stick it in [mumbles] ... slices.

Teacher: We have to keep it separate. They have to go in two separate boxes. (*Still irrelevant.*)

[The teacher used Brian's pizza model and, moving some of the pieces, asked where were the 12 slices.]

Brian has now abandoned his "theory" but now Scott also seemed to lose confidence in *his* "theory." The mood of the session began to change at this point. The boys submissively seemed to comply to the teacher's directions, almost in anticipation of what their expected reply should be.

Scott: But my theory was wrong.

Brian: Yeah ...

Teacher: Hmm. Now it says we're gonna get one piece from each of the two pizzas..

Scott: [Yawns] We're gonna need 7 pieces.

Brian: We're gonna hafta get more than that.

Teacher: Well, one student gets one piece from each pizza, [Scott nods], and there's 7 students ...

Scott: Yeah, and they're each gonna get 7.

Teacher: ... and each getting that, right?

Brian: [as he is still working] but, they could have more slices than that, cause there's gonna be more slices left over.

Scott: Yeah, but then it would, it would be equal—but then there would be a slice left over for Mrs. Elson [the teacher referred to in the problem].

Brian commented about the extra slices that were left over and Scott responded, suggesting that the teacher in the problem could have some slices. It seemed that the boys were questioning the problem statement and turned to their teacher for clarification. Her response was to direct Brian and Scott to distribute the slices. Brian removed the blocks that represented the slices; Scott then counted the slices that were taken.

Brian: [to teacher] So do we have to count Mrs. Elson?

Teacher: No, we just have to count what it says in the, in the problem.

Brian: [arranging the blocks] Scott, I think I need a little more than this.

Scott: Oh, OK, I think we can handle that [together the boys reach for the blocks].

Brian: I think I'm really gonna need a little less than this. [Scott made a noise and Brian mumbled, inaudibly; Scott responded, also, inaudibly.]

Teacher: OK, now show me what, what's, who's getting what here.

Brian and Scott together indicated the assignment of pieces of pizza to the 7 children from each pie. The episode continues:

Brian: OK, we counted the kids from this class, like [Brian repeats the assignment of names for pizza slices for the 7 students.]

Teacher: Uh-huh.

Brian: So, [He counts 7 pieces with Scott's help and removes them].

Teacher: Uh-huh.

Brian: So these, these would be gone.

Teacher: So that's their, their pieces from the pizza number one?

Brian: Yeah. So then ...

Scott: Then their pieces from number 2 ...

Brian: Some left over but then she wants to take from this pizza (*points*). So here's the ... 6 kids and [mumbles inaudibly removing the tiles].

Teacher: OK.

Brian: So this would be left.

Teacher: [pointing to the model] So these are all the slices that are being given to the, the kids?

Brian: Yeah.

Teacher: The 7 kids. OK, so it's that much. All right, now let's see if we can count up how many slices.

The teacher asked how many slices were in a pie. She was finally successful in directing Brian and Scott to the solution she apparently was looking for—fourteen twelfths (which was, of course, an incorrect answer). Then she drew a picture of the model, instructed the boys to shade the picture, and directed Brian to indicate the slices.

Brian: 14

Scott: [simultaneously] 14.

Teacher: 14, and how many slices made 1 whole pizza?

Scott: 7

Teacher: No, how many slices [pointing to one yellow hexagon].

Brian: There're 12.

Scott: There're 12, yeah, there're 12.

Teacher: Made a pizza. So we're using up 14-12ths, right?

S & B: [simultaneously responding] Twelfths.

Teacher: Let's put down 14-12ths.

Brian: So it would be one.

Teacher: All right..

Brian: And 2-12ths.

Scott: Equals one.

Teacher: It says [reading the problem] "what fraction," so is what we figured out [pointing], 14-12ths, so let's leave that answer.

Brian: OK.

Note that, once again, the teacher was unable to get a correct reading of Brian's representation—he was apparently trying to make quantitative sense out of the answer, by putting it in the terms that would be most meaningful to him. The teacher did not recognize this goal, and insisted upon the formal answer "fourteen twelfths."

Analysis of Teacher-Student Representation Mismatch

One of the most striking features of this tape is the mood change in the two boys, when they abandon the initiative, self-reliance, and confidence of their early work, in the face of the disagreement with the authority of the teacher. The passive receiving of teacher direction by both Brian and Scott is quite apparent. Was the teacher's representation of the problem data so intense that it obstructed her consideration of the alternate data representation built by Brian? She clearly had trouble building an appropriate representation to match Brian's. In her analysis of the lesson, she wrote:

> After noticing a need to further develop the concept of mixed numbers, this sheet was created. Scott saw right away that 14/12 was eaten, but Brian decided this was 14/24.

The teacher's lesson plans indicated that the session involved representing fractions as mixed numbers. Perhaps she intended to write a problem whose solution was to be a mixed number. It is difficult to know. Surely, she would not expect that the students would eat more pizza than the total that was available. She might not have recognized that her interpretation did not fit the statement of the problem because her own schema for "unit" had not yet been firmly built. It is interesting that she choose not to confront Brian with the conflict between his choice of unit and her own. Was it because she was unsure?

Or, perhaps she was trying to be less directive in her teaching and very much believed that Brian's reasoning was faulty. She may have been so convinced of Brian's incorrect solution, that she chose to "help" him by relating the problem to the way she was representing it in her own mind. Notice how she directed his attention to the way pizzas were packaged. This has the appearance of a desperation attempt to get Brian to change his representation to be more like hers. It is also possible that her prior assessment of Brian's understanding also may have influenced her lack of receptivity to his current thinking.

It is likely that there is no simple explanation for this mismatch in teacher-student representation. Multiple factors may be contributing, some of which might include the following:

1. The teacher intended to make up a problem situation that would provide an opportunity for the students to construct a model for adding two fractions whose sum would be an improper fraction. In order to achieve this, she needed *one* pizza to serve as the *unit*. Instead, however, she wrote a problem which called for *two* pizzas as the unit, which, in turn, called for the building of a model to determine a fraction in quite a different way.

2. Her earlier assessment of Brian's (and other students') lack of understanding in adding fractions influenced her receptivity to the students' current thinking. In her assessment of the Pizza Lesson, she wrote: "Brian continues to add the denominators." (Note also her predilection for interpreting arithmetic as symbol-manipulation.)

3. The teacher's schema for unit concept might not have been sufficiently developed, or she had not retrieved a well developed schema for unit, because if she had, she might have been looking to see whether they were using the same unit. For example, she might have asked "What unit are you using?" The choice of language suggests what unit one has retrieved.

Long Term Effects

One might ask what are the short and long term implications for such a mismatch of problem situation for both teacher and students. For the teacher, who was later confronted with the episode by a staff member, who had an opportunity to talk about it, and who was able to learn from it, there was an opportunity to address the complexities of language and of writing problems and listening to students. For Brian and Scott, there turned out, in fact, to be no long term damage.

Approximately one year later, Brian and Scott were independently interviewed and given the same Pizza Problem to solve. Pattern Blocks and other familiar manipulatable materials were available for use. The interviews were video-taped and a recorder kept written notes for each session.

In separate interviews both boys indicated that they remembered working together the year before but did not remember how they solved the Pizza Problem. The boys were now in different mathematics classes and no longer had an opportunity to work together. Interestingly, neither boy used the pattern blocks to solve the problem.

Scott began by drawing two circles and partitioning them into sections, and when offered the blocks, chose two yellow hexagons for the pizzas, but solved the problem mentally:

Int: [Interviewer asks:] Do you understand the problem?

Scott: Yeah. The 12, they had 2, Miss Elson ordered 2 large pizzas that were split into 12 pieces [draws two circles and begins partitioning the area into sections; seems to have trouble making twelve].

Int: I think you made 8 slices.

Scott: Yeah, I did.

Int: That's all right; you can make more if you like.

Scott: [tries to make 12 equal sections in his circles] And then.

Int: Do you use these anymore? [pointing to blocks]

Scott: Yeah, sometimes ...

Int: You can do them anyway you want. With blocks?

Scott: I can do 'em both.

Int: OK. Either way. I'd like to see both, too.

Scott: And they ordered two pizzas [selects 2 yellow hexagons] and then, eh, and then 7 students had one pizza each.

Int: From each pizza.

Scott: Yeah, so that'd be, then they would take both pizza ... had 12 slices ... so that would be 24 and the students ate 14 slices.

Int: Uh-huh

Scott: So then you'd have 10 slices left because 24 minus 14 is 10 ... you would have 10 slices left.

Int: OK. What fraction?

Scott: 10/24.

Int: Is that how much you ate or how much you had left?

Scott: How much you had left.

Int: How much did you eat? What fraction ?

Scott: 14/24.

Int: Did you remember how you did the problem last time?

Scott: No.

Brian, on the other hand, chose to use a picture and numbers to solve the problem. After Brian read the problem, the following discussion took place:

Int: Remember arguing with him [Scott] about this?

Brian: No

Int: How would you do it? You can use blocks, you can use numbers, you can draw a picture.

Brian: There're 12 slices in the two pizzas [rereads the problem; draws 2 circles and marks 12 sections each]. So what fraction was eaten? How much was left over?

Int: How much was eaten?

Brian: Oh! 14/24.

Int: You don't remember doing the problem with the pattern blocks last year?

Brian: I can remember that problem, but I don't remember doing it.

What occurred with Brian and Scott was that they were *not* ultimately influenced by the teacher's solution. Their own knowledge, that is the logic of their own thinking, was what remained durable over time. It seemed that Brian and Scott did not remember, transfer or apply information that had no meaning to them.

Conclusions

Two aspects deserve comment. First, we have here almost the quintessential defining alternatives. One way is to try to know as much as we can about the students' ideas; try to understand the students' thinking; and try to help students develop their thinking further. The other choice is to largely ignore the students' ideas.

Second, if we *do* decide to work with the students' ideas, notice how very hard this is. Indeed, in the Brian and Scott example, the teacher's interpretations do not match the student's thinking.

How significant is it that teachers be aware of students' thinking about a mathematics problem? We argue that it is *very* significant—in fact, essential. Paying attention to the mathematical thinking of students engaged in active mathematical constructions, and trying to make sense of what students are doing and why they are doing it, is prerequisite, we believe, to gaining insight into the nature of the development of children's representations. Observation and analysis of children's constructions while working on sets of problem situations for particular mathematical concepts can provide teachers with children's verbal, pictorial and symbolic descriptions of them. This knowledge can provide a fundamental way to assess understanding of those concepts. Knowledge of children's thinking in this regard provides the basis for the creation of appropriate activities that have the potential to encourage even further learning. A teacher's failure to recognize the way a student is thinking about a problem can at the very least end up by wasting time in mutual misunderstandings.

We contend, therefore, that it is important that teachers continuously strive to estimate the nature of children's representations. Teachers' knowledge of children's thinking makes it possible for them to challenge and extend students' thinking and appropriately modify or develop activities for students.

This particular episode suggests to us the power of a student's own mental representations and the logic of the student's own thought processes. The incorrect interpretation which the teacher had, in the previous year, attempted to persuade the boys to accept did *not* pose any problem. Indeed, since the boys had, in Piaget's sense, no assimilation paradigms for what the teacher had been saying, her words seem largely to have been ignored. The evidence of their own senses, and of their own thought processes, seem to have carried the day, and led them to a correct understanding of this problem.

Such a view implies a radically different role for teachers, one in which they must develop the skill and confidence to develop and implement lessons that are based on the interaction of mathematical ideas between teacher and student. This calls for assessment of individual children's learning on the basis of their mathematical behavior within these problem-solving environments. It suggests that not only is it important for teachers themselves to build representations of mathematical ideas but also it is important that they try to understand the nature of children's constructions, *especially* when they do not match their own (see Postscript). Deep rooted behaviors in teaching that focus on giving information to students are hard to change. Looking carefully at mathematics and how children learn may suggest that teachers seriously consider alternatives. Perhaps the mathematics classroom can become a learning environment for *both* teacher and students.

Postscript

Nel Noddings raised the question: "Suppose that the students' representations had been wrong. Would the teacher's correct interpretation then have been as quickly brushed aside?" Our response is that we expect it would have been. There is considerable evidence suggesting that attempts to remediate and correct children's errors have been successful in the short term with little, if any, long term success. Perhaps this is because most remediation occurs in a show and tell format followed by rote drill and practice. What seems to be a more promising approach is for the teacher to try to understand what the students were doing and why, and then to provide them with an opportunity to see their own faulty reasoning.

PART THREE

CONSTRUCTIVISM IN THE CLASSROOM

Chapter 7: Discovery Learning and Constructivism

Robert B. Davis
Rutgers University

Recent years have seen two large-scale efforts at improving the curricular goals and pedagogical methods of school mathematics by placing greater emphasis on student experience, on good analytical thinking, and on creativity. The first of these was proclaimed (incorrectly) to have been a failure. Will our present-day sophistication, as represented by today's constructivist perspective, mean that the second attempt will prove any more successful? What, precisely does constructivism mean for a classroom teacher? It is said that "those who do not study history are doomed to repeat it." This is all too likely to be true in the case of reforming school mathematics. Consequently, in the present chapter, we take a more careful look at the previous effort, and try to understand how things may be different the second time around.

In the four decades since World War II there have been two major efforts to modify school science and mathematics so as to put greater emphasis on the thoughtfulness and creativity that are often seen as the hallmarks of true science. The first of these occurred in the 1950's, and bore the names of projects such as P.S.S.C., SCIS, E.S.S., and the Madison Project, and of individuals such as Jerrold Zacharias, Francis Friedman, Marion Walter, Caleb Gattegno, Frances and David Hawkins, David Page, Geoffrey Matthews, Leonard Sealey, and Robert Karplus. The mathematics parts of these various projects were lumped together with other efforts of quite different sorts and this unlikely combination was given a single label: "the new mathematics." If one looked at the totality of these projects it is probably true that the only thing that they all had in common was that every one of them proposed major changes in the then-typical versions of school mathematics. Some of these projects used manipulatable physical materials, others did not. Some sought to build up mathematical ideas gradually in students' minds, whereas others attempted to "get it right from the very beginning." Some focussed on various uses of mathematics, whereas others dealt only with what might be called "pure mathematics." [1] Putting such different approaches together, and trying to treat them as one single thing, made useful analysis nearly impossible, and in fact the world seems to have learned very little from this quite large investment of time, effort, and money. Even worse, most of what has been "learned" is in fact wrong.

Most readers, if they have heard of the "new math" at all, have heard that it was installed in a large number of US schools in the 50's and 60's, and turned out to be a failure. Both claims are false, and so is the implied third claim that there ever was such a thing as "the new mathematics ." Given the diversity,"even the irreconcilable differences—that separated the different efforts, there clearly was *no* identifiable curriculum or set of goals or pedagogical approach that could be thought of as well—defined and testable. But if, as this chapter does, I select a few of these projects that *did* have something in common, then the approach represented by these projects was never tried in most US schools. It was, however, adopted in a small percent of our schools, and in every reported case where it was conscientiously employed and carefully evaluated, it proved remarkably successful. Far from proving that the "New Math" was not successful in classrooms, the data from the 50's, 60's, and 70's show quite convincingly that *there is a better way to help students learn mathematics,* and in fact *we actually know—at least roughly—what it is.*[2]

Something did, indeed, fail—but it was *not* the best of the school programs, it was the *analysis* of this important episode in American educational history. The present short chapter cannot hope to rectify all of the errors and misconceptions that we seem to have "learned" from this experience, but perhaps it can begin the process of rethinking what really happened, and why it did.

Why the Analysis Failed

I argue that the *analysis* of these curriculum improvement ventures failed for at least four reasons.[3]

1. the *lumping—together of disparate interventions* (as discussed above);
2. *traditional expectations* that were far different from the goals and methods of the new programs;
3. the *lack of an adequate theory* for discussing these differences;
4. the need to give more prominence to *actual classroom episodes.*

A More Appropriate Focus

We can avoid the error of inappropriate lumping-together of dissimilar interventions by choosing carefully the projects that are considered, and making sure that the chosen group of "curriculum improvement projects" do, in fact, have much in common. For a selection of projects that were quite similar in their basic assumptions and goals, I choose: the Madison Project (see, e.g., Davis, 1988a), David Page's Illinois Arithmetic Project, the EDC-based Elementary School Science Project ("ESS"), Robert Karplus' SCIS project at UC Berkeley, and the California state-wide Miller Math Program .[4] Interventions in this same spirit occurred in Great Britain, in the work of Leonard Sealey, Edith Biggs, and the Nuffield Science Project, among others. The same fundamental approach was agreed to by most of those who worked on these ventures, and in fact there was considerable sharing of resources and even personnel. Probably the best over-all description of this work is that given in Howson, Keitel, and Kilpatrick (1981; see also Biggs, 1987; Davis, 1988a; and McNeill, 1988).

What did these projects claim to have in common? From things written and said at the time, their goals included these:

1. To get each student to see mathematics as a reasonable response to a reasonable challenge.

2. To get each student to see mathematics as *worthwhile* and *rewarding*.

3. To get each student to see mathematics as a subject where it was appropriate to *think creatively* about what you were doing, and to try to *understand* what you were doing.

4. To get each student to see mathematics as a subject where, in fact, it was possible to understand what you were doing. (There is abundant evidence that most U.S. students do *not* usually see mathematics in this light, nor is it taught in such a way that understanding is really possible.)

5. To give students a wider notion of what sorts of things make up the subject of "mathematics." (There is overwhelming evidence that most students think that "mathematics" refers only to meaningless rote arithmetic.[5]) For example, these projects included science activities that use mathematics, several approaches to geometry, algebra, the use of computers, probability, and mathematical logic.

6. To let students see that mathematics is *discovered* by human beings, that their own classmates and they themselves can discover ways to solve problems if they take the trouble to think about the matter and if they work to understand it.

7. To give students a chance to learn the main "big ideas" of mathematics, such as the concept of function and the use of graphs.

8. To have students see mathematics as a useful way of describing the real world. (It is quite different to see mathematics as a description of the real world, instead of seeing it as the process of *following a set of meaningless rules,* which, unfortunately, *is* how most students view mathematics.)

Pedagogical approach

With some variations between projects, these efforts mainly tended to use the pedagogical approach of creating an appropriate assimilation paradigm for each new idea they sought to teach. Thus, for example, the Madison Project introduced positive and negative numbers by using an activity called *Pebbles in the Bag*, where a bag, initially containing an unknown number of pebbles, has pebbles *added to it* or *removed from it*. The question is never "How many pebbles in all are there in the bag?"—that remains unknown—but rather "How many *more* pebbles are now in the bag?" or "How many *fewer* pebbles are there in the bag?" Thus,

$$6 - 5$$

would correspond to "putting 6 pebbles into the bag, and then removing 5."

We would not know how many pebbles were in the bag at that point, because we did not know how many were in the bag at the beginning, but we would know that there was one ***more*** pebble in the bag than there had been when we started. Hence we would write

$$6 - 5 = {}^{+}1,$$

where the "positive one," $^{+}1$, means that there is **one *more*** pebble in the bag as a result of these actions. It does *not* mean that the total number of pebbles in the bag is *one*. Suppose, instead, we had put 5 pebbles into the bag, and then removed seven. We would describe this action (note this instance of the theme "mathematics as a description of reality") by writing

$$5 - 7,$$

and we know that the result would be having two ***fewer*** pebbles in the bag than we had when we started, so we would write

$$5 - 7 = {}^{-}2,$$

where the symbol negative two ($^{-}2$) means two less than we had before.

What does this accomplish? Because the children are readily able to visualize the action of "putting five pebbles into the bag, and taking seven out" (remember that the bag did not start empty, but had a goodly collection of pebbles in it at the outset), *they have this visualization available to them as a tool that lets them think about the mathematics*. The Madison Project called this an assimilation paradigm, and the strategy of basing teaching on this approach was called the paradigm teaching strategy. (For a more extended discussion, see Davis, 1984, Chapter 21.)

This same approach—the creation of an assimilation paradigm by providing appropriate experience—is used also by an important present-day program, the middle school mathematics program being created in Atlanta, Georgia, by Robert Moses, where the Atlanta subway system is taken as the basis for the fundamental idea of direction implicit in positive and negative numbers.

If one did not give the children something like this "assimilation paradigm," they would have no way of thinking about the mathematics, and any expectation that they would *invent* methods of solution would be unreasonable. The children are, however, perfectly capable of thinking about bags and pebbles and "putting pebbles into a bag" and "taking pebbles out of a bag." If we use this as a basis for thinking about mathematics—which is perfectly reasonable if one takes the position that mathematics is a description of reality—then it is entirely possible for the children to carry out their own analyses of problems, and to invent their own methods of solution.[6] We have given them *tools* to *think* with!

Expectations

It should be clear from the preceding discussion that the expectations of these curriculum improvement projects were quite different from the common expectations of most parents, teachers, or even students. Even when the projects believed that they were explaining themselves reasonably clearly, their words probably meant something different to most hearers. An example may make this clearer:

Most of these projects described themselves as trying to have the teacher focus on the *task* or *problem,* and *to do this at a fundamental level.* But this phrase was probably often misunderstood. How were these projects *different* from usual school practice, which might also be described by this same phrase? Consider the introduction of base three numerals, as used by the Madison Project. Two small groups of children are asked to communicate messages back and forth, but they must pretend that *nobody can count above three.* One group of children—at the front of the room, say—is then given a pile of tongue depressors (let's say that you and I know that there are twenty-two tongue depressors in the pile). The children at the front of the room must send messages to the other group of children (at the back of the room) so that the second group can assemble *exactly the same number* of tongue depressors.

How can one tell if the job has been done correctly? That part is easy; after the second group has assembled what they believe is the correct number of depressors, the two collections can be brought together and a one-to-one matching can be attempted.

But what kind of messages can the first group of children send? Remember, *nobody can count beyond three.* The children, however, are given some things they may use: rubber bands, plastic sandwich bags, and shoe boxes, among other things. The task of solving the problem is left for the children to work out.

Sooner or later they do this, by counting three depressors and putting a rubber band around them to make a "bunch," continuing until as many bunches have been made as possible. (If there really were twenty-two depressors, the children will make seven bunches, and there will be **one** separate tongue depressor left over that is not part of a bunch, as shown in Figure 1.)

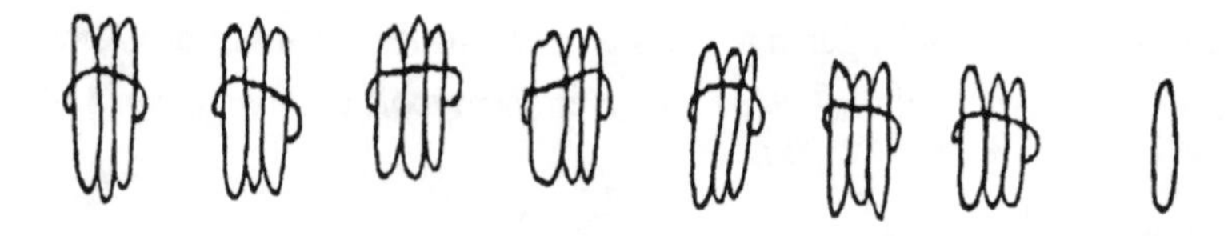

Figure 1 - Twenty -one Tongue Depressors Tied in Bunches of Three

But there are too many bunches for the children to be able to tell the others how many there are—nobody can count beyond three, remember?

However, what worked once can be tried again: count three bunches and put them together into one plastic sandwich bag. Continue until you have filled as many bags as possible. (Under our assumption that there were twenty-two depressors, you should now have two filled bags, one bunch that is not in a bag, and one loose tongue depressor, as shown in Figure 2.)

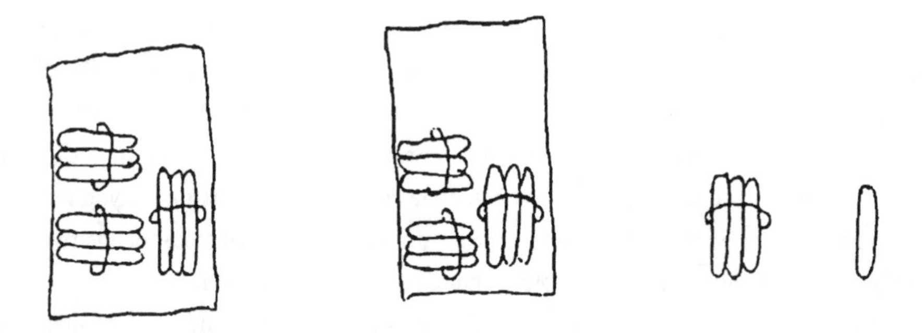

Figure 2 - Bags of Bunches of Tongue Depressors

We have finally arrived at a message that can be sent to the group at the back of the classroom, *without anyone needing to count beyond three*. While the children can in fact be depended upon to invent a solution to the basic problem, they cannot be expected to invent history. *After* the children have solved the problem, the teacher needs to intervene at the stage of interpreting what they have accomplished, and helping them to devise a succinct notation (which, of course, will look very much like standard base-three numeral notation; see Figure 3 for the message that the children might send).

sandwich bags 2

bundles 1

loose tonge depressers 1

Figure 3 - Representing Bunches of Tongue Depressors with Numerals

In the language used by the projects, this was a case of focusing on the basic task, and leaving it up to the children to invent a way to solve it. This, in fact, is where place-value numerals come from—they are an elegant solution to an important problem: how can you name a very large number of different numbers by using only a small number of different words? Furthermore, how can you do this so that the names that you will make up for the numbers will reflect the nature of the numbers so accurately that one can use the names themselves in order to work out actions that really involve the numbers.

Let's contrast this with a more typical classroom lesson that might also seem to satisfy that same description of "focussing on the *task* at a *fundamental level* ." Among other things we will see how it was possible for teachers and parents to be confused by what they read and heard. Let us once again use a task involving place-value numerals, perhaps the task of subtracting

1,002 - 25.

A typical school approach might say: "I can't take 5 from two, so I regroup" (or "borrow," or whatever the local language might be). The teacher might say: "Cross out the 1 and write a small 1 next to the zero, so we'll think of it as *ten.*" (See Figure 4.)

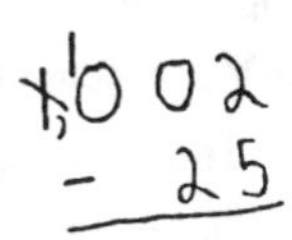

1,[1]002
- 25

Figure 4 - Initial Step in Regrouping or Borrowing

The teacher might continue: "Now cross out the *ten* and write a *nine* over it, and write a small *one* next to the next zero." (See Figure 5.)

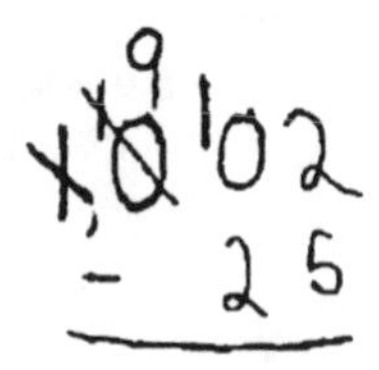

Figure 5 - Consecutive Applications of Regrouping or Borrowing

Might one not describe *this* approach, also, as focusing on the basic task? What could be more "basic" than focusing on exactly the things that you need to write down on the paper?

But of course these written marks are *not* what is really basic. They are merely a way of keeping track of what *is* really basic—the number of things that you have, or the number of things that are being taken away, and so on. These manipulations of written symbols *must* seem arbitrary, because the meaning is *not* present right there in the symbols—not in the way that it *is* present in the physical tongue depressors. When you put 21 tongue depressors into bunches of three each, you *must* (if you do it correctly) end up with seven bunches. Nobody needs to tell you that—you cannot do it any other way. The logic is right there in the tongue depressors themselves, and it is compelling.

By focusing on meaningless manipulations of symbols, the typical school curriculum gives a student no effective mental symbol system that carries the basic logic of the real situation. The "logic" of rote manipulations has the appearance of being arbitrary—indeed, as far as its intrinsic internal structure is concerned, it is arbitrary. Nothing in the child's everyday experience has built up a "symbol system of necessary implications" that can function in the way that the child's symbols for pebbles and for taking pebbles out of a bag can. Each student knows that if you take some pebbles out of the bag, there will be fewer pebbles remaining within the bag. The student does not need to make a special effort to remember this. There is no need to keep repeating to oneself "Remember—when you put pebbles *in* there will be *more* pebbles in the bag. When you take pebbles *out* there will be *fewer* pebbles in the bag. When you put pebbles *in*." The student's mental symbol system for pebbles and bags and putting into and removing *does* have a fully developed intrinsic logic that compels certain outcomes and prohibits others—just as reality does, *because this symbol system was drawn from experience with reality*.

How shall we describe the difference between the curriculum improvement projects and typical school practice? Clearly, they are built on different assumptions—but it might no be far-fetched to claim that the difference is in epistemological assumptions. *The intervention projects made different assumptions about the nature of knowledge*. In the view of the projects, you know something when you have powerful mental representations, not merely for "surface level" aspects, but also for the deeper level constraints and possibilities, in much the way that each child knows that the act of putting more pebbles into the bag will have the result of *increasing* the number of pebbles in the bag; *the child's mental symbol system makes this clear to him or to her.*

The value of such a mental symbol system becomes evident when one tries to think about a problem for which one has no such powerful system. Consider, for example, the physical apparatus shown in Figure 6, consisting of a spool of thread that can roll on a table top.

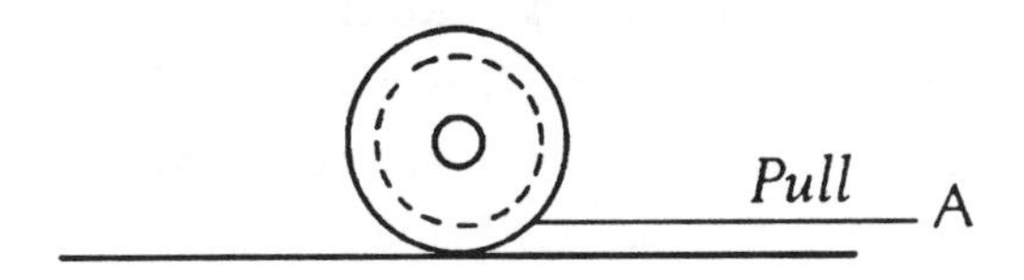

Figure 6 - Spool of Thread on a Table

If the thread at Point A is pulled to the right, what will the spool do? Most people find this problem hard to think about, because their mental symbol system for representing situations like this is not sufficiently well developed.

Traditional school practice viewed "learning mathematics" as a matter of learning, usually by rote, certain meaningless rules for writing meaningless symbols on paper in some very specific ways. This kind of knowledge could only be acquired by being told and by practicing it. The projects viewed "learning mathematics" as a matter of building up, in your mind, certain powerful symbol systems that allow you to represent certain kinds of situations, and a matter of acquiring skill in creating such mental representations and in using them. This kind of skill is not easily acquired by being told; here, too, you have to practice, but it is *not* the tedious practice of rote arithmetic. It might better be described as practice in *thinking*.

That these are quite different assumptions about the nature of *knowledge* becomes clear to anyone who will consider a few examples. They also imply differences in how one would test to see what knowledge the child had acquired. Traditional school practice tests mainly *the ability to repeat back* what has been told or demonstrated. For the innovation projects, this was not a satisfactory method of determining whether or not a student had acquired appropriate mental symbol systems, and could use them in a powerful way. The emphasis that the projects placed on studying how a student attacks a *novel* type of problem *for which he or she has not been given specific advance preparation* arose because only *novel* problems were seen as testing the power of one's mental representation systems. Clearly, since such situations are new, they *cannot* be dealt with by merely "doing what you were told to do." Your mental representations must give you the power to see new possibilities and new constraints in new situations.

The difference between these alternative views of "knowledge" has been revealed in stark terms in some recent studies of testing practices, and studies of how some school programs prepare children to take tests. Koretz (1988) reports the case of a school mathematics supervisor who noticed that the state's minimum competency test presented *shaded figures* to accompany questions asking that one find the *area*, and presented *unshaded figures* for questions asking about *perimeter*. Koretz reports that, based on this observation, the supervisor instructed the teachers to tell children to *multiply* the numbers in problems where the figure was shaded, and to *add* the numbers in problems where the figure was not shaded. This is typical of a kind of strategy that *raises test scores* ***without*** *actually teaching the relevant concepts, skills, or understandings*.

This approach is nearly the antithesis of what the intervention projects intended. Contrast this strategy with the work of Edith Biggs in helping children learn the concept of area (Biggs, 1987). What mental symbols do students need, if they are to think about what "area" really is? They need to be able to visualize some appropriate square units (some projects used square pieces of paper for this); they need to be able to visualize placing these squares carefully in place (much as one puts down square tiles on a floor), they need to be able to visualize cutting tiles into smaller pieces when necessary (because things do not always come out even!, and—if they are to have a more complete idea of area—they need to be able to visualize some process of "taking limits" as one does in calculus (because sometimes even smaller pieces cannot be made to fit exactly). They also need to have a mental symbol system that lets them distinguish two-dimensional problems from three-dimensional problems, and they need to know that "area" *refers to a two-dimensional attribute*. None of this, of course, was developed by the "multiply if shaded, add if not" rule that was told to those children.

Developing a suitable kind of mental symbol system is so critical for the effective learning of mathematics, and has proved so elusive in efforts to describe what is needed, that a second example may be in order. Suppose this time that the task were to solve an equation of the form:

$$x/a = b/c.$$

The typical classroom lesson usually seeks to teach the method of "cross-multiplying." The teacher carefully shows the children that the number in position "c" is to be multiplied by the number (perhaps an "unknown") in position "x," and the number in position "a" is to be multiplied by the number in position "b," producing the result shown in Figure 7.

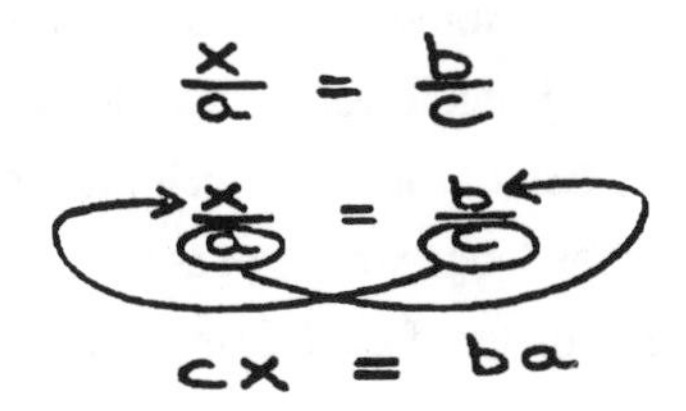

Figure 7 - Illustration of the Method of Cross-Multiplying

Because of the pattern in which the symbols appear, this is often called *the method of cross-multiplying*. Is this lesson helping the students to develop an appropriate mental symbol system? We would argue that it is not. To be sure, the students probably *are* developing a mental representation for where symbols can be written on the paper—but this, again, is merely a *surface-level phenomenon*, and the relationships on this level are not representative of the true constraints and the true possibilities in this problem.

Here, as in the previous example, one wants mental representations for the deeper-level structure. In this case, what is really involved is the equality of two numbers, or the request that some number be chosen so that two numbers will in fact be equal. But whenever two numbers are equal, the double of one would equal the double of the other—that is, if you doubled each number, the results would again be equal. There is nothing gratuitous or arbitrary about this—it is basic to how numbers themselves actually behave. Nor is this limited to doubling. If you multiplied each number by three, the results would be equal. Or if you multiplied each number by ten. Or if you multiplied by seven and one half. What the students need to develop, if they are to deal with such situations in a powerful way, is a set of mental symbols that show such operations as "multiplying each side of an equation by the same number," "adding the same number to each side of an equation," and so on.[7] A student who has developed mental representations for this aspect of how numbers behave can easily invent for himself or herself methods such as the "cross-multiply" method. They are a simple consequence of the way numbers work. But the converse is not true; a student who has learned "cross-multiplying" will not necessarily see *why* this method works, nor *how numbers themselves behave*.

Constructivism

In the 1950's and 1960's, when the so-called "curriculum improvement projects" were most active, and were being poorly implemented and incorrectly analyzed, one never heard of "constructivism." The dominant psychology was "stimulus-response" theory, which held that a concern for what was going on in someone's mind was unscientific, because it speculated about matters that were essentially unknowable. The dominant teaching strategy was to show or tell students what to do, and then to supervise their practice while they attempted to repeat what they had been shown. Knowledge was seen as the ability to regurgitate facts and to imitate rituals. "Testing" was a matter of confirming the accuracy of this regurgitation or imitation.

The scientists, mathematicians, and teachers who created the curriculum improvement projects knew, from their intuitive analysis of their own personal experience, that this misrepresented the true state of affairs. They were, in fact, able to devise interventions that produced far more effective learning in their students (see, for example, Dilworth, 1973). What was not readily available, however, was conceptualization of the process of learning mathematics—a *formalized* conceptualization, that went beyond the *intuitive* conceptualizations that many of the individuals did possess, based on their own personal experiences. Anyone who observes mathematics education has to be impressed by the quite sudden eruption of "constructivism" as a central concern of so many researchers. I would argue that while its origins may be somewhat obscure and uncertain, the reason for it is perhaps clear. It is a strong response to the very great need for a better way to think about how human beings deal with the subject called "mathematics."

Notes

1. For a more detailed discussion of the differences among these various efforts, see Davis, 1988a, or Howson, Keitel, and Kilpatrick, 1981.

2. One version of the kind of program described here was evaluated by Robert P. Dilworth (see Dilworth, 1973; NACOME, 1975, pp. 93-94). This very careful evaluation showed that children taught by teachers who had studied in this program *did* perform better, both on tests of conceptual understanding and on tests of computational skill. Furthermore, students taught by teachers who had studied in the program for *two* years did better than students taught by teachers who had studied only *one* year (so the second year of study by the teachers did pay off in improved performance of their students). Dilworth went even further; he tested children a year later—when at least one year had elapsed after the teacher had studied in the program—and found that the gains were still there. The teachers *were continuing* to have a superior effect on children whom they taught; the improvement in teaching effectiveness was not temporary.

A program of this sort—an extension of the Madison Project program—was put on the computer-assisted system PLATO at the University of Illinois, and was evaluated by ETS. In Figures 8 and 9 I reproduce, in a form developed by John Gilpin, the results of one year of student experience with the PLATO computer-delivered lessons. In the Gilpin diagrams, each arrow represents one child; the tail of the arrow is the child's performance on the Comprehensive Test of Basic Skills at the beginning of the school year (reported in so-called "grade level equivalents"); the point of the arrow is that same child's performance at the end of the school year. Hence, each arrow represents the progress made by one child. Figure 8 shows the Gilpin report for a control class. Figure 9 shows the report for one of the PLATO classes. The difference is dramatic, and strongly in favor of the new curriculum.

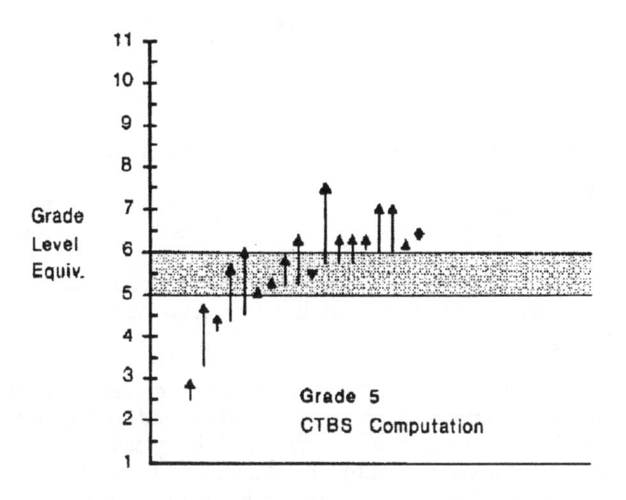

Figure 8 - Gilpin Diagram for a Control Class. Each arrow represents one child.

3. Remember, it was the analysis that failed; the interventions themselves did *not* fail.

4. The interventions listed were most visible in the 1950's and 1960's although some of them continue up to the present time. Very active and effective versions of this approach are still available, especially through programs offered by Marilyn Burns Education Associates (21 Gordon Street, Sausalito, California 94965, Tel. (415) 332-4181). The work of Seymour Papert on LOGO environments is in this same spirit, augmented by the use of computers (see, e.g., Papert 1980).

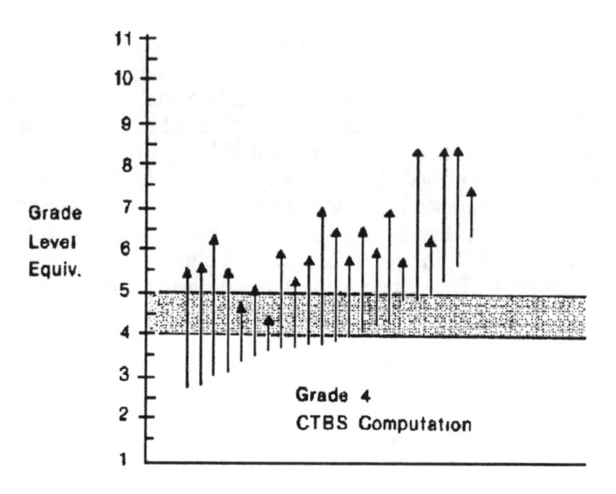

Figure 9 - Gilpin Diagram for a PLATO Class. Each arrow represents one child.

5. One excellent, but not generally available, piece of evidence is the collection of videotaped interviews with children assembled by Eve Hall, Elizabeth Debold, and Edward Estey, of Children's Television Workshop. The impact on the viewer of hearing these children describe what they are learning as "mathematics" is both striking and painful; few viewers can escape wondering why our society finds it appropriate to subject young people to this sequence of experiences.

6. Indeed, one of the most controversial aspects of these projects in the 1950's and 1960's was their claim that children could *invent their own methods for solving problems*. But the basis for the popular skepticism may lie not so much in questions about the nature of children as in questions about the nature of mathematics. Clearly, if you see mathematics as the process of following some meaningless rules that you have been taught to imitate, then there is no possible way that you could "invent" these rules, no more than you could "invent" the English language. Arbitrary historical accidents cannot be "invented." But if, instead, you see mathematics as a process of working out reasonable responses to reasonable challenges, then it becomes entirely possible to invent your own methods—indeed, nothing else would really make sense. This possibility becomes all the more real if the instructional program is careful to give you tools for thinking about the mathematics, in just the way that the "pebbles-in the-bag" activity gives a child some tools for thinking about positive and negative numbers.

7. To have a truly effective way of dealing with such problems, the students also need a good representation system for the truth values of mathematical statements. For details, see Davis (1988b).

Chapter 8: What Constructivism Implies for Teaching

Jere Confrey
Cornell University

In this chapter, a critique of direct instruction is followed by a theoretical discussion of constructivism, and by a consideration of what constructivism means to a classroom teacher. A model of instruction is proposed with six components: the promotion of student autonomy, the development of reflective processes, the construction of case histories, the identification and negotiation of tentative solution paths, the retracing and group discussion of the paths, and the adherence to the intent of the materials. Examples of each component are provided.

An Analysis of Direct Instruction

The form of instruction in mathematics that has been most thoroughly examined has been "direct instruction" (Good &Grouws, 1978; Peterson, Swing, Stark and Waas, 1984; Rosenshine, 1976). With this form of instruction, one finds a relatively familiar sequence of events: an introductory review, a development portion, a controlled transition to seatwork and a period of individual seatwork. I suggest that three key assumptions about mathematics instruction underlie direct instruction and are subject to challenge from a constructivist perspective:

1. Relatively short products are expected from students, rather than process-oriented answers to questions; homework assignments and test items are accepted as providing adequate assessment of the success of instruction.

2. Teachers, for the most part, can simply execute their plans and routines, checking frequently to see if the students' responses are within desirable bounds, and only revising instruction when those bounds are exceeded (Peterson & Clark, 1978; Snow, 1972).

3. The responsibility for determining if an adequate level of understanding has been reached lies primarily with the teacher.

There has recently appeared an increasing amounts of evidence that direct instruction may not provide an adequate base for students' development and for student use of higher cognitive skills. Doyle, Sanford and Emmer (1983) examined students' views on the "academic work" in traditional classrooms and found that, as students convince teachers to be more direct and to lower the ambiguity and risk in classroom tasks, the teachers may inadvertently mediate against the development of higher cognitive skills. Other challenges to direct instruction come from the research on misconceptions (Confrey, 1987) wherein researchers have documented severe student misconceptions across topics and achievement levels. These misconceptions appear to be resistant to traditional forms of instruction (Clement, 1982; Erlwanger, 1975; Vinner, 1983). These studies point to a need to develop alternative forms of instruction.

Efforts to develop forms of instruction that overcome misconceptions have focused on the need to have students make their conceptual models explicit (Baird & White, 1984; Lochhead, 1983a; Novak & Gowin, 1984; Nussbaum, 1982). Instructional models to encourage problem solving in the classroom have emphasized the need to help teachers take risks and to develop flexibility in the subject matter (Stephens & Romberg, 1985). All of this research shares a commitment to the importance of an active view of the learner. The philosophical approach that argues most vigorously for an active view of the learner is constructivism.

Constructivism

A theory that seems to be a powerful source for an alternative to direct instruction is that of constructivism (Confrey, 1983, 1985; Kelly, 1955; von Glasersfeld, 1974, 1983, this monograph). Put into simple terms, constructivism can be described as essentially a theory about the limits of human knowledge, a belief that all knowledge is necessarily a product of our own cognitive acts. We can have no direct or unmediated knowledge of any external or objective reality. We construct our understanding through our experiences, and the character of our experience is influenced profoundly by our cognitive lenses. To a constructivist, this circularity is both acceptable and unavoidable. One's picture of the world is not, however, static; our conceptions can and do change. The essential fact that we are engaged in living implies that things change. By coordinating a variety of constructions from sensory inputs to meditative reflections, we adapt and adjust to these changes and we initiate others.

A consequence of a constructivist's denial of direct and assured access to "the way things really are" is that authority resides in the persuasiveness of one's argument and in how well one marshals evidence in support of a position. Constructivists recognize that these forms of argument also exist within the culture of discourse. Although constructivism is often equated with skepticism, the skill the constructivist must truly develop is flexibility. While it is accurate to say that the constructivist rejects any claim which entails the correspondence of an idea with an objective reality, the most basic skill a constructivist educator must learn is to approach a foreign or unexpected response with a genuine interest in learning its character, its origins, its story and its implications. Decentering, the ability to see a situation as perceived by another human being, is attempted with the assumption that the constructions of others, especially those held most firmly, have integrity and sensibility within another's framework. The implications for work with students are stunning.

Piaget provided an essential key to a constructivist perspective on teaching in his work, wherein he demonstrated that a child may see a mathematical or scientific idea in quite a different way than it is viewed by an adult who is expert or experienced in working with the idea. These differences are not simply reducible to missing pieces or absent techniques or methods; children's ideas also possess a different form of argument, are built from different materials, and are based on different experiences. Their ideas can be qualitatively different, which can sometimes mean that they make sense only within the limited framework experienced by the child and can sometimes mean they are genuinely alternative. To the child, they may be wonderfully viable and pleasing. They will not be displaced by any simple provision of the "correct method," for, by their existence for the child, they must have served some purpose. Before children will change such beliefs, they must be persuaded that the ideas are no longer effective or that another alternative is preferable.

When one applies constructivism to the issue of teaching, one must reject the assumption that one can simply pass on information to a set of learners and expect that understanding will result. Communication is a far more complex process than this. When teaching concepts, as a form of communication, the teacher must form an adequate model of the students' ways of viewing an idea and s/he then must assist the student in restructuring those views to be more adequate from the students' and from the teacher's perspective.

Constructivism not only emphasizes the essential role of the constructive process, it also allows one to emphasize that we are at least partially able to be aware of those constructions and then to modify them through our conscious reflection on that constructive process. As Toulmin (1972) wrote "(Wo)Man knows and (s)he is conscious that (s)he knows" (p. 7). (Parentheses added.) Thus, not only can we assert that a constructive process is involved in all acts of perception and cognition, but also that we can gain a measure of access to that constructive process through *reflection.*

In mathematics the *reflective process,* wherein a construct becomes the *object* of scrutiny itself, is essential. This is not because, as so many people claim, mathematics is removed from everyday experience. It is because mathematics is not built from sensory data but from human activity (mathematics is a language of human action): counting, folding, ordering, comparing, etc. As a result, to create such a language we must reflect on that activity, learning to carry it out in our imaginations and to name and represent it in symbols and images. Reflection, as the "objectification" of a construct, functions as the bootstrap by which the mathematician pulls her/himself up in order to stabilize the current construction and to obtain the position from which the next construct can be created. Mathematicians act as if a mathematical idea possesses an external, independent existence; however the constructivist interprets this to mean that the mathematician and his/her community have chosen, for the time being, not to call the construct into question, but to use it as if it were real, while assessing its worthiness over time.

Frequently, constructivism is criticized for being overly relativistic. The argument is that, if everyone is a captive of their own constructs, and if no appeal to an external reality can be made to assess the quality of those constructs, then everyone's constructs must be equally valid. Two replies to this argument are offered. First, the constructive process is subject to social influences. We do not think in isolation; our choice of problems, the language in which we cast the problem, our method of examining a problem, our choice of resources to solve the problem, and our acceptance of a level of rigor for a solution are all both social and individual processes. Thus, a constructivist assumes there are shaping influences on his/her constructions. The criteria for assessing the strength of an individual's construct are discussed later in the section on powerful constructions.

Secondly, a person can never know what another person's constructs are with any certainty. Communications between people function in two ways: people try to assess the congruency between their constructs through their use of language, choice of references, and selection of examples; concurrently, they try to assess the strength of the other person's constructs as an independent system by considering the apparent level of internal consistency of those constructs. For example, in mathematics education a teacher needs to construct a model of a student's understanding given what the student knows, while gauging how like the teacher's own constructs the student's constructs are. Thus, a teacher must always give consideration to the possibility that a student's constructs, no matter how different they appear from the teacher's own constructs, may possess a reasonable level of internal validity for that student and therefore must adapt the instruction suitably.

Comparing mathematics to a tool is perhaps useful in seeing how mathematics is not a description of an external reality, but is, on the contrary, a human construction, invented to achieve human purposes. Consider a common tool such as a spoon, a can opener or a computer. A tool is always used to act on something else, to shape it or to move it. It has an impact on the object; its role is not neutral. One does not come to know a tool through a description of it, but only through its activity. Its structure and its function are interrelated. A powerful tool is one of broad application. If it is too specialized or too inaccessible to use with ease, it will fall into disuse. Anthropologists examining ancient cultures found tools to have been durable and to have been tied into the daily lives of the individuals in a culture in essential ways. A tool is designed to save people effort. Once one gains facility in its use, one gains time to undertake further activities. Mathematics is such a tool and its changes reflect the changes in the kinds of activities human beings are engaged in.

Thus, as a constructivist, when I teach mathematics I am not teaching students about the mathematical structures which underlie objects in the world; I am teaching them how to develop their cognition, how to see the world through a set of quantitative lenses which I believe provide a powerful way of making sense of the world, how to reflect on those lenses to create more and more powerful lenses and how to appreciate the role these lenses play in the development of their culture. I am trying to teach them to use one tool of the intellect, mathematics.

Some Implications for Mathematics Instruction

A constructivist theory of knowledge has dramatic implications for mathematics instruction. It follows from this theory that students are always constructing an understanding for their experiences. The research on students' misconceptions, alternative conceptions, and prior knowledge provides evidence of this constructive activity. From a more knowledgeable vantage point, we can claim that these constructions of our students are weak; they both lack internal consistency and explain only a limited range of phenomena. As mathematics educators, we must thereby promote in our students the development of more powerful and effective constructions. To do this, we must define what is meant by a more powerful and effective construction and attend to how the promotion of these constructions might be achieved.

I want to suggest that the most fundamental quality of a powerful construction is that students must believe it. Ironically, in most formal knowledge, students distinguish between believing and knowing. To them there is no contradiction in saying, "I know that such and such is considered to be true, but I do not believe it." To a constructivist, knowledge without belief is contradictory. Thus, I wish to assert, that *personal autonomy is the backbone of the process of construction.*

In addition to the necessary quality of commitment by the construer, a powerful construction exhibits other significant qualities. The list which follows is intended to be illustrative, not exhaustive. Powerful constructions are typically characterized by:

1. A structure with a measure of internal consistency;
2. An integration across a variety of concepts;
3. A convergence among multiple forms and contexts of representation;
4. An ability to be reflected on and described;
5. An historic continuity;
6. Ties into various symbol systems;
7. An agreement with experts;
8. A potential to act as a tool for further constructions;
9. A guide for future actions; and

10. An ability to be justified and defended.

Students of mathematics often apply only one criterion to their evaluation of their own constructs, asking "is it in agreement with the experts?" (Or, in less constructivist terms, "Is it right?") As a result, their knowledge of mathematics becomes isolated and formalized from the rest of their experience, which is constructed from their action on the world in a more spontaneous and interactive fashion. Memorization and imitation of examples produce the "right answer," the desired outcome, in a local, well-defined problem space and thereby outpace the more difficult endeavors of constructing the idea and of coordinating its interactions with the other qualities of powerful constructions. The thesis of this paper is that students must learn to construct powerful ideas and that this constructive process requires the coordination and convergence of the ways of knowing identified in the above list of the qualities of powerful constructions.

An Alternative Set of Assumptions

Constructivism commits one to teaching students how to create more powerful constructions. Variations are expected and nurtured, and the student is given primary responsibility for assessing the quality of a construction. The goal of instruction can be stated as:

> An instructor should promote and encourage the development for each individual within his/her class of a repertoire for powerful mathematical constructions for posing, constructing,exploring, solving and justifying mathematical problems and concepts and should seek to develop in students the capacity to reflect on and evaluate the quality of their constructions.

This goal suggests acceptance of three assumptions:

1. Teachers must build models of student's understanding of mathematics. To do this, teachers need to create as many and as varied ways of gathering evidence for judging the strength of a student's constructions as possible. The result will be that a teacher creates a "case study" of each student.

2. Instruction is inherently interactive; through their interactions with students regarding their knowledge of subject matter, teachers construct a tentative path upon which students may move to construct a mathematical idea more consonant with accepted mathematical knowledge. Teachers, however, must already be prepared for the likelihood that the students' constructions will not coincide with their own, and encourage the students' expression of their beliefs so that teachers come to understand student beliefs. Teachers then must be prepared to revise their own beliefs or to negotiate with the student to find a mutually acceptable alternative (which may or may not endorse the conventions of mathematical practice). If the student advocates a solution that is clearly lacking adequate argument, teachers will need to signal firmly that, in their judgment, the student's position lacks legitimacy.

3. Ultimately, the student must decide on the adequacy of his/her construction.

Using these alternative assumptions, an examination of a teacher with constructivist beliefs is undertaken in the second part of the article. Specific examples of the methods used by this outstanding teacher are provided, with a more detailed discussion of each of the assumptions.

The Context

The study took place at the SummerMath program, an experimental summer program for young women in high school offered by Mount Holyoke College. The program, described in earlier papers (Confrey, 1983), has explicit constructivist underpinnings. Most of the young women who attended were academically capable but had experienced difficulties with mathematics. Since no scholarships were available at the time, the students were, for the most part, upper middle class or wealthier. Follow-up evaluations of the program indicate that students' scores on SAT (math) showed considerable improvement and that alumnae report they are more persistent, more confident, and ask more questions.

The intent of this study was to construct a model of the practices of a teacher committed to constructivist beliefs. The instructor was selected for his excellence in teaching, as evaluated by the students in the program for two summers and confirmed again during the third year, the year of the study. He consistently received strong evaluations both at the end of the program and in follow-up evaluations four months later.

The study was conducted during the second of six weeks of the program. A class entitled Fundamental Mathematics Concepts, Level I, was selected for investigation. The topic for the week was the representation of fractions; the materials were designed to reveal misconceptions and to promote the coordination of arithmetical manipulations of fractions with actions on pictures. The eleven young women in the class ranged from ninth to eleventh graders. In order to be in this class, the student had to have scored less than 45% on a multiple choice placement test made up of twenty-five items from the high school curriculum.

Frequently the organization and pace of the class differed significantly from typical classrooms. The students in the class worked in pairs on the curriculum materials provided each day. Using the paired problem solving method of Whimbey and Lochhead (1980), the students took turns solving the problems. One student was supposed to talk through the problem while the other asked questions about the method. Often, in spite of one week of focused training on the method, the students would solve the problems together.

In this study, the focus is on the teacher-student interactions. The data are taken from videotapes of these interactions. Consistently on the videotapes one sees that the students do most of the talking and writing. The pace at which the content is covered is dramatically slower than in traditional classes; it is not unusual for the students to solve only two or three problems in a class.

The Method

The model for the research is described by Donald Schon (1983) in his book, *The Reflective Practitioner*. Schon argues that the professional engages in an art of practice which is not easily or accurately characterized by a technical analysis. He searches for an "epistemology of practice implicit in the artistic, intuitive processes which some practitioners do bring to the situations of uncertainty, instability, uniqueness and value conflict" (p. 49).

Schon developed the idea of "reflection in action." He suggested that much of the practitioner's knowledge is tacit; it operates on his/her actions, decisions and judgments but cannot be stated under the usual circumstances. However, when stimulated to reflect on those actions through surprise, puzzlement, or perhaps intention, the practitioner may ask questions such as: "What features do I notice when I recognize this thing? What are the criteria by which I make this judgement? What procedures am I enacting when I perform this skill? How am I framing the problem?" In answering these questions tentatively, the professional, according to Schon, "also reflects on the understandings which have been implicit in his action, understandings which he surfaces, criticizes, restructures and embodies in further actions" (p. 50).

In concert with Schon's perspective, a researcher (who also taught in the program) and the teacher together examined the teacher's practice. No attempt was made to identify predetermined categories for discussion in the interviews. The intent was to try to develop, through the use of videotapes, a model of this particular teacher's instruction which was acceptable to both the teacher and the researcher.

To this end, for five days the class was videotaped for its hour and a half duration. Two students in the class were selected and paid to be interviewed each day, and their work was collected and copied each day. They were also asked to keep journals over the summer session. Each afternoon of the five days, the instructor and the researcher discussed the day's instruction. Each day the instructor would describe what he felt were significant issues, would specifically describe his interactions with the two students who were to be interviewed, and then would view portions of the tape, answering the researcher's questions and commenting on portions that he recalled as significant. The focus was on explaining how he viewed his role in the class. The interview lasted from sixty to ninety minutes daily.

For the last four days of the study, after the interview with the instructor, the researcher would interview separately the same two students who worked together every day in class. This interview would begin with a clinical interview on one of the problems discussed on the tape. Then the taped interactions between the instructor and these students would be viewed and discussed with an emphasis on what the student thought the instructor said or meant. The interviews lasted from forty-five minutes to an hour.

The Results

The results of the study will be presented in the form of a model of the teacher's instruction. The following six components of the model will be described and illustrated:

1. Promotion of autonomy and commitment in the students;
2. Development of students' reflective processes;
3. Construction of case histories;
4. Identification and negotiation of tentative solution paths with the student;
5. Retracing of those solution paths; and
6. Adherence to the intent of the materials.

For each component, specific techniques used by the teacher will be discussed and illustrated with examples drawn from the videotapes and the interviews.

1. Promotion of Autonomy and Commitment

Earlier I stated that personal autonomy is the backbone of the process of construction. Baird and White (1984) argued that a significant improvement in student learning depends on "a fundamental shift from teacher to student in responsibility for, and control over, learning" (p. 2). In this teacher's interactions with students, he consistently demanded that the students make a commitment to their answers. He used four techniques to accomplish this goal: he questioned students' answers whether they were right or wrong; he insisted that students engage in a problem at least to the extent of explaining what they had tried; he would remain with a group long enough to get them started in a potentially productive direction; and he emphasized the importance of having a student evaluate his/her own success. The following quotes from the interviews with the teacher illustrate these techniques:

> But, she's given me nothing to work from other than saying, "You only give us stuff that is too hard for us to do, and we are stupid." I can't deal with that until she starts putting forth effort, and that gets a starting point to discuss what she understands and what she doesn't understand. Why? She's got to get over that herself.
>
> If I stand there, they are going to continually look up at me to see if every line they draw at this point is right. I'm leaving them there; let them see what they can do with what's left [after I walk away].
>
> The students have a success, and one way to treat that is, we can tell them they've just had a success. But they've got to sit there and go, "I've just

> done this all by my little old self." I think that's the point that's very important. It's their reflection on what "I've done," what they've done, and their admission they've done something; they've beaten the problem.

The need to increase the level of student autonomy in relation to mathematics is continually addressed in this teacher's instructional methods. He believed that a measure of autonomy is a prerequisite to developing the self-awareness one needs to be a successful problem solver. Once a student began to take responsibility for her thinking, the teacher felt that he could move to develop her powers of reflection.

2. Development of Students' Reflective Processes

I posited that reflection is the bootstrap for the construction of mathematical ideas. In order to promote a student's awareness of her problem solving, the teacher asked three categories of questions, which correspond roughly to the three stages of construction posited in Confrey (1985): the problematic, action and reflection. In that work, I indicated that, for students to modify and adapt their constructions, they must: (1) encounter a situation that they experience as personally problematic, as a roadblock to where they wish to be; (2) act to resolve the problematic, often using multiple forms of representation and (3) assess the success of their action in resolving the problematic or determine what problematic remains. In this teacher's instruction, there was evidence that he used three levels of questioning to increase his students' awareness of their own strategies and methods. Each level is discussed and illustrated.

Level One: The Interpretation of the Problem. These questions involved the request to reread or restate the question. The teacher would ask the students questions such as, "What are we doing?" "What is the problem?" or "What does this problem say?" In asking these, the teacher would often focus the student's attention on *the language the student was using*. These questions appear deceptively simple to an observer; for the students, it was often difficult to repeat the problem or describe it in any fashion. The students appeared so unaccustomed to speaking mathematically that the questions on this level served a subtle and essential role. Furthermore, it was apparent that the students' responses to this level of questioning had a significant impact on their success in solving the problem. Often what sounded to the listener to be multiple rereadings of the problem had the effect of curtailing the amount of time the student needed to undertake a solution to the problem, possibly indicating that what was verbalized as repetition represented significant cognitive processing on the part of the student.

Level Two: Cognitive Strategies. The teacher would ask a student to describe what she was doing. When working with students at this level, he would use the level of precision of the student's statements as a standard, requesting slightly more. He would not allow the students to introduce mathematical terminology or formulae without explaining them to him. In one interview he commented, "I think one of the things that happens as students learn to relate to teachers is that they come close, and teachers fill in the blanks." A typical teacher/student interaction, in which they discuss pictorial comparisons of 13/5 and 21/10, illustrates Level Two questioning. The student is currently attempting to draw a picture to compare 2/3 and 5/7 and contrasting it to the solution strategy she used to solve 13/5 and 21/10:

Teacher: How did we do the fifths and the tenths?

Student: But those were in proportion.

Teacher: What do you mean, "in proportion?"

Student: Not proportion; they were equal. At least, um, I mean they weren't equal, but—I know what I mean.

Teacher: I know what you mean too, but now you'll have to tell me.

Student: I mean, I can't think of a word. I mean five is half of ten; therefore we divided the fives in half. It would be just like adding five more. I don't know how to explain it. I mean you have like five parts and you divide it in half, and it was like double. But like if you took three things and divided it in half, you'd have six things and not seven. Therefore, I mean, you'd have a different problem.

When the teacher requires the student to explain her meaning of proportion, she reveals her tendency to think of an increased denominator as an additive operation, and then she revises her approach to a multiplicative one, doubling. If she had continued to think of the change from fifths to tenths as additive, the change from thirds to sevenths would have posed no difficulty, but her method would most likely have failed. After this exchange, the student pair and the teacher work on a method to divide the rectangle vertically in thirds and horizontally in sevenths to make units of twenty-firsts and compare their relative size.

Level Three: Justification of Strategies. Once a student was able to tell the teacher what the problem was about and how she was going about solving it, the teacher began to ask the student to defend her answer. Again, the level of rigor demanded depended on the knowledge the teacher had of the student; he demanded an explanation which adequately fit the student's interpretation of the problem and the methods and strategies she had constructed.

Examples of the questions he used included: "Why? What does that tell you? What can you tell me? Why not?" and "What do you mean it doesn't work?"

The development of the students' reflective processes was a primary goal of this teacher's instruction. Generally he used three questioning strategies to develop these processes. Much of his time was spent asking students to discuss their interpretation of the problem and to describe precisely their methods of solution. Once they had carefully described their interpretation and methods, he asked students to defend their answers. Two characteristics of his interactions were prevalent: a focus on the language used by the students, and an acceptance and exploration of the students' visions of the problems. He worked primarily within his understanding of their framework, and in order to do this effectively, he developed a model to allow him to understand a particular student's case.

3. Construction of a Case History

Not only did questioning of the students promote their reflection, it allowed the teacher to gather substantial knowledge and insight into their understanding of mathematics. The teacher often spoke of a student's general tendencies in problem solving, and used this information to design appropriate solution strategies. Because this knowledge involved cognitive, affective and personal dimensions, we developed the habit of referring to this as the teacher's construction of a case history. As pointed out by Cobb and Steffe (1983), researchers and teachers alike build models of their students' mathematical knowledge, attempting "to 'see' both their own and the children's actions from the children's point of view" (p. 85). Models which can be used effectively to interpret the students' performances over time can be thought of as case histories (e.g., Confrey, 1983; Erlwanger, 1973).

Although no elaborate case history can be provided here, a brief summary might be helpful. One of the two students who participated in the interview, Joyce, consistently rejected the use of pictures, relying heavily on borrowed algorithms and half-remembered rules. On the first day of class, the teacher commented that he was having some difficulty getting this pair of students to draw the pictures. On the second day, the student had difficulty solving a ratio problem. She abruptly switched and tried to use a percent, still unable to explain what the problem was about. The teacher commented that she was overworking the problem. In the interview, he explained his comment, saying:

> What I am trying to get her to do is to see that she can think her way through the problem . . . without heading off into Percent Land or whatever. That she can think her way through it and will have a fair idea of what's going on without working the problem. The reason I say that is, in working with her the last few days, her tendency is to use those poorly taught algorithms from arithmetic whenever possible. You drop one in, and something comes out, and you say, "Oh, something came out; I'm happy," and you have no idea what's going on.

In the interview with Joyce, she expressed her ambivalence with the drawing of pictures and described the differences in this type of instruction:

I don't know exactly how it would work if you would have to, like in algebra; you have different types of formulas and things like that. When you come across a problem like that it seems to me you would need a formula, and it's not something that you would just figure out on the spur of the moment, without going through a really long, extensive proof or something like that.

On the last day of the study, the teacher discussed his evaluation of Joyce's situation:

Teacher: I'm really stuck. I don't know how to get her off that, and I don't really think that I can. I really think that she has got to make the decision that the way she has been learning math in terms of algorithms is not helping her. Her reliance on calculation is really not helping her. Until she decides and makes that recognition, the best we can do is just try daily to break her of it. [I can] Say, look at it this way, and she will probably sit there and draw the pictures [for me]. [And] She will sometimes do it [for herself].

Researcher: Were you discouraged?

Teacher: No it's going to take her a while. I mean, what are we doing? We're taking two weeks of experience in drawing pictures and trying to downset against nine years of "It's important to do the calculations quickly in your head." She may or may not come around. I will keep hoping that, eventually, when she sees more and more examples of her algorithms falling down because she looks at the way a result comes out and she doesn't like they way the result looks, so she questions the algorithms.

By interacting with the students primarily in one-on-one (or -two) settings, the teacher was able to form a powerful model of the students' characteristic approaches to solving problems. In order to do so, he created multiple sources of evidence from which to build his models, using his interactions with them, their performance on key items from the curriculum, and his observations of their interactions with the other students.

At this point of the paper, our model of this teacher's instruction appears relatively static; he has created a powerful model of the student's mathematical ideas, he has insisted on her autonomy, and he has focused her thinking on her own thinking, increasing her powers of reflection. We might ask, "when does he begin to teach?" In asking this, we find ourselves back in a traditional interpretation of teaching as "telling." In fact, as one examines the videotapes of this instruction, it appears that he is indeed teaching already, for the students are learning to solve these problems successfully, often as a result of their interactions with him.

Perhaps this "progress" on the part of the students was attributable to the particular context. It could be claimed that, since the topic was the representation of fractions, the teacher is remediating, not teaching new material. I think the question of whether this instructional model is useful in teaching new material must remain an open question in need of further examination. In many ways, I would argue that, for these students, this was new material. Furthermore, I suggest that, if it does indeed prove true that the model seems to be most appropriate for "remediation," its value is still not easily dismissed. Our elementary and secondary curriculum has massive amounts of repetition built into it, simply because the students never learn or retain what they have been taught.

This teacher's instruction was concerned with challenging and changing his students' current conceptions. The teacher would try to aid the student in building a more powerful construction, from the student's point of view. Because the teacher's own constructions formed the framework for examining student constructions, their influence on the direction of the interaction was unavoidable. However, as evidenced by the substantial variation witnessed in the solution paths, the teacher's conceptions were either very flexible, possessing multiple perspectives, or were in fact altered over the course of the interactions. Because of the students influence on the method of solution, I have labelled this component of instruction as the identification and negotiation of a tentative solution path.

4. Identification and Negotiation of a Tentative Solution Path

At times, the teacher was unable to promote a successful resolution of a problem using the techniques cited above. However, from the information gained from this questioning and from his broader knowledge of the student's case, he would have developed a model of the student's understanding of the problem. Assuming that he judged that the student was investing enough initial effort, he would intervene more directly.

From the tapes and the interviews, there was evidence that he would analyze the difficulties he anticipated the students might have with the problem and then, with his knowledge of the student's case, he would develop a tentative solution path and negotiate it with the student. Since he would typically select certain conceptually difficult problems and review them with all students, the researcher could analyze the differences in his approach. The variety of methods used from group to group substantiated the need to conceptualize a more interactive and negotiated view of his classroom. As the teacher commented, "You can't walk into class saying, 'I know I'm going to do it this way.' "

Thus, this teacher would gather evidence on which he could build a model of how the student was thinking about the problems. From this model, he would construct a tentative solution path. At a more global level, he would be building an understanding of the student's "case." As he worked towards a solution with the student, he would test the adequacy of his models of the student's theories and of his case history. The results of these tests could lead to a revision of his tentative solution path. Over the course of the week, there were changes in how students responded. As they became more autonomous and confident, they influenced to a greater extent the direction and outcome of the interaction.

One set of strategies was designed specifically to encourage the student to form a more powerful construction as described earlier. These included relating the ideas to other concepts, challenging students' use of symbols and the English language to communicate their ideas, pushing towards consistency within a related set of concepts, limiting the scope of the idea to allow for a local resolution of the ideas, asking for representations, or exploring the idea from multiple perspectives. He often introduced a measure of cognitive conflict in order to promote the construction of more powerful ideas.

Some of the variety of questions he asked can be illustrated by a listing in which the reader is advised to attend to the form rather than the particular substance: "How does that relate to what you were seeing up here? Is there anything you did in the last one that can help you with this one? What if I colored in seven boxes? *This* doesn't look like *this*. Can you do something similar? Which am I to believe, your picture or your diagram?" These questions invite the student to attend to a previous issue, to resolve conflicts and to find analogies between different episodes.

At other times, the instructor would provide the student with more directed guidance in solving the problem. Through the use of product-oriented questions, the teacher would move a student towards a solution. These occasions seemed to arise: 1) when the student's tolerance for frustration was low; 2) when the student needed to experience success or progress; and/or 3) when the class as a whole needed closure on a topic.

Such decisions appeared to produce unreliable outcomes. At least once when the teacher was more directive with the two interviewees, the interviews revealed that the students' understanding of the material was weak and sketchy. There did, however, seem to be some evidence that such a decision to provide directed guidance even with deleterious *cognitive* consequences may be important *affectively* in order to lower a student's frustration level and to encourage her to be willing to engage in the problem-solving process at a later time.

5. Retracing and Reviewing the Solution Path

When the problem was solved, the instructor would revisit the problem with the student. This strategy of "re-viewing" the problem was useful for providing: 1) opportunities for reflection; 2) an overview of the problem; 3) occasions for the teacher to advocate for his view of mathematics teaching and learning; and 4) the student with a sense of accomplishment. Examples of the questions he used in reviewing solution paths included: "Isn't that what your picture says? How do you decide? How do you know when to reorganize?"

6. Adherence to the Intent of the Materials

Too many people assume that constructivist teaching implies a *laissez-faire* attitude on the part of the teacher. Teachers learning to teach within this framework, fearing that they will "tell too much," often remain silent, while the students flounder in frustration. They mistakenly believe that a constructivist teacher lacks a specific agenda for what is to be learned in the classroom. Such a characterization did not apply to this teacher. He was committed to a particular view of mathematics learning and found many opportunities to share this with the students.

During the week, the teacher was determined to have the students come to see that one can make sense of fractions using pictures, and that the algorithms for rational numbers can be seen as actions on those pictures. If a student chose to approach an understanding of the problem which did not use pictures, the instructor would allow her to complete the investigation, but then he would relate that solution to the representation of fractions. He strove to do this without undermining the student's initiative

Conclusions

In this paper, the assumptions behind direct instruction were examined and questioned from a constructivist perspective. After discussing constructivism, alternative assumptions for instruction were offered. Then, using videotapes of four days of instruction and methods of clinical interview and stimulated recall, I examined the practice of one teacher in the constructivist tradition who seemed exemplary from a variety of measures. A model of this particular teacher's instruction was presented and discussed. The purpose of the work was to suggest that alternative forms of instruction can exist in mathematics that differ in their basic assumptions from the tradition of "direct instruction."

PART FOUR

CHILDREN AND THE EDUCATION OF TEACHERS

Chapter 9: Classrooms as Learning Environments for Teachers and Researchers

Paul Cobb, Terry Wood and Erna Yackel

Purdue University

This chapter describes research that is attempting to coordinate a constructivist view of learning mathematics with the practice of teaching for the purpose of analyzing children's mathematical learning within the setting of the classroom. The chapter also is an attempt to transport research on learning from a constructivist perspective from the laboratory to the environment of the classroom. In so doing, the classroom also, unexpectedly, became a learning environment for the project teacher as well as the students. The teacher's experiences, that provided opportunities for her learning and transformed her beliefs about her role and the students role, are described and interpreted. These experiences influenced the researchers such that teacher development has become a primary focus along with children's learning. The researchers' current perspective and their approach used with teachers, which differs significantly with traditional procedures, is described.

The focus of our research and the emphasis of our development work has been on second graders' construction of mathematical knowledge in the setting of classroom instruction. As such, our primary interest has been in the processes by which children create mathematical meaning in the course of classroom social interactions. Our work has been influenced in general by Piaget's and von Glasersfeld's constructivist epistemology that emphasizes the role of cognitive conflict, reflective abstraction, and conceptual reorganization in mathematical learning (Piaget, 1970a, 1980a ; von Glasersfeld, 1988). At a more specific level, we have drawn on the cognitive models of young children's construction of arithmetical knowledge developed by Steffe (Steffe, Cobb, & von Glasersfeld, 1988; Steffe, von Glasersfeld, Richards, & Cobb, 1983).

Theoretical Perspective

Although Piaget's theory provides a general explanation of cognitive development, it was intended to address epistemological issues (Fabricus, 1979) and, as a consequence, considers only broad areas of intellectual development. His theory therefore constitutes a general orienting framework but leaves much unsaid about the nature of cognitive development in

---

The research reported in this paper was supported by the National Science Foundation under grant numbers MDR 874-0400 and MDR 885-0560.

specific conceptual domains. Not surprisingly this has posed major difficulties for educators who have attempted to develop pedagogical implications from Piaget's ideas about learning. The cognitive models developed by Steffe and colleagues (1983, 1988) extend the work of Piaget by offering an explanation of children's cognitive development in areas directly relevant to elementary school mathematics. In particular, these models specify ways in which children might construct increasingly sophisticated concepts of number, position, addition, subtraction, and place value numeration. This elaboration of Piaget's general theory of cognitive development makes it possible to consider children's construction of mathematical knowledge in a way relevant to instructional issues (Thompson, 1985).

This constructivist approach to cognitive modelling, while offering an account of the psychological processes involved in children's mathematical development, has tended to downplay the importance of social interaction in the learning process. As Smedslund (1977) commented:

> In so far as Piagetian psychologists focus on logicality as a variable (e.g., conserver or non-conserver) and give only peripheral attention to the problem of determining children's understanding of instructions and situations, I think they are making an epistemological error and are out of step with everyday human life as well as with all useful psychological practice. (p. 4)

In this regard, our work has also been influenced to some extent by Vygotsky's (1962, 1978) analysis of the crucial role that social interaction plays in learning. Like Piaget, Vygotsky views learners as an active organizers of their experiences but, in contrast, he emphasizes the social and cultural dimensions of development. One of the most frequently quoted passages from Vygotsky's writings is his formulation of what Wertsch (1985) called the "general genetic law of cultural development" (p. 60).

> Any function in the child's cultural development appears twice or on two planes. First it appears on the social plane, and then on the psychological plane. First it appears between people as an interpsychological category, and then within the child as an intrapsychological category . . . Social relations or relations among people genetically underlie all higher [cognitive] functions and their relationships. (Vygotsky, 1978, p. 57)

In this general characterization of development, internalization is a process involved in the transformation of social phenomena into psychological phenomena. Consequently, Vygotsky saw social reality as playing a primary role in determining the nature of intrapsychological functioning (Wertsch, 1985). Vygotsky has clearly made a profound contribution to our understanding of intellectual development by attempting to relate cognitive and social phenomena. However, the key explanatory process of internalization functions as an undefined primary construct in his theory and has resisted subsequent attempts to elaborate its workings. In contrast, the work of Blumer (1969), Mead (1934), and Schutz (1962) dispenses with the notion of internalization and instead focuses on the processes by which people interpret each other's actions and thus achieve compatible meanings. From this perspective, social interaction is not a source of processes to be internalized. Instead it is the process by which individuals create interpretations of situations that fit with those of others for the purposes at hand. In doing so, they negotiate and institutionalize meanings, resolve conflicts, mutually take others' perspectives and, more generally, construct consensual domains for coordinated activity (Bauersfeld, 1988; Bishop, 1985; Blumer, 1969; Maturana, 1980b; Perret-Clermont, 1980). These compatible meanings are continually modified by means of active interpretative processes as individuals attempt to make sense of situations while interacting with others. Social interaction therefore constitutes a crucial source of opportunities to learn mathematics in that the process of constructing mathematical knowledge involves cognitive conflict, reflection, and active cognitive reorganization (Piaget, 1970a). As such, mathematical learning is, from our perspective, an interactive as well as constructive activity (Cobb, 1988).

Research Emphases

As initially conceptualized, our research objective was to analyze young children's mathematical learning in a classroom where instruction was broadly compatible with constructivism. Our original intention was to extend the methodology of the "constructivist teaching experiment" (Cobb & Steffe, 1983; Steffe, 1983) to the complexity of a public school classroom by conducting a classroom teaching experiment. We planned to analyze individual children's construction of mathematical knowledge as they interacted with the teacher and their peers. In the process of undertaking these analyses we became aware that the classroom had simultaneously and unintentionally become a learning environment for the teacher. As the teacher used the instructional activities in her classroom and interacted with her students, her beliefs about her own role, the students' roles, and the nature of mathematical activity changed dramatically (Wood, Cobb, & Yackel, in press). It was by analyzing her learning that we developed an initial, tentative understanding of classrooms as learning environments for teachers. This chapter is our attempt both to provide an unsanitized account of the learning opportunities that arose for the teacher and to reflect on how our observations of her learning have influenced our current approach to teacher development.

The Classroom Teaching Experiment

The one-on-one constructivist teaching experiment extends Piaget's clinical interview methodology by including teaching episodes that enable the researcher as teacher to investigate more extensively the processes by which a single child constructs mathematical knowledge (Cobb & Steffe, 1983; Steffe, 1983). During the clinical interview, the researcher attempts to infer the child's current mathematical ways of knowing. Teaching episodes follow in which the researcher attempts to provide opportunities for the child to learn by judiciously selecting tasks, offering suggestions, and posing questions. In this situation, the researcher/teacher interprets the child's mathematical activity and thus elaborates and tests a provisional model of the child's cognitions. The tentative model is then used to guide the creation of new situations in which to further investigate the child's learning.

The constructivist teaching experiment methodology is ideally suited to the purpose of investigating the processes by which children might construct mathematical knowledge. However, it tends to emphasize the cognitions of individual children at the expense of social interaction. In the course of the analysis, for example, the researcher focuses almost exclusively on what the child might be thinking and implicitly takes the social process of mutually negotiating the interview situation for granted. Our research and development project in second grade was an attempt to extend the methodology of the one-on-one constructivist teaching experiment to the classroom and to coordinate cognitive and social analyses. To this end, a classroom teaching experiment was conducted for the entire school year during which we had to address all the objectives for second grade mathematics set by the participating school corporation. Throughout the experiment, the teacher was a full member of the project staff and made her own decisions about how to use the instructional activities in her classroom. We, for our part, visited the classroom each day to video-tape both small group work and whole class discussions. These recordings constitute the primary data source for our analysis of the children's construction of mathematical knowledge as they interacted with each other and the teacher during the mathematics lessons.

At the outset, we anticipated that the classroom teacher would conduct her mathematics lessons in a manner similar to that of the researcher in the one-on-one teaching episodes. Our initial expectation was that the teacher would construct models of her students' mathematical understandings as she interacted with them. She then would use these models to generate conjectures about the children's potential mathematical constructions and, on this basis, select instructional activities and interact with them in ways that might give rise to opportunities to construct mathematical knowledge. In the course of these teaching episodes, we anticipated that she would test and, when necessary, revise her interpretations of children's mathematical understandings (Steffe, 1986, 1988; Stevens & Collins, 1980). We initially believed that it might be feasible for the teacher to interact with twenty or more students in this manner in that the children typically attempted to solve the instructional activities in small groups and then participated in a teacher-orchestrated whole class discussion of their solutions. This instructional approach provides opportunities for the children to construct mathematical knowledge not found in traditional classrooms (Cobb, Wood, & Yackel, in press) and for the teacher to observe and discuss with the children their interpretations of and solutions to the instructional activities. We speculated that this might make it possible for the teacher to develop models of her students' mathematical understandings that could be used to inform her pedagogical interventions.

The instructional activities were developed in the course of the experiment on the basis of on-going observations of children's mathematical activity in the classroom. Given the central role we attribute to children's personal experiences, we were well aware that, historically, child-centered curriculum efforts have been strongly criticized for engaging children in activities in which the "subject matter" is lost (Thompson, 1985). It was here that the models developed by Steffe proved to be of greatest value in that they account for children's mathematical experiences rather than their cognitive behaviors. We therefore drew on the models in an attempt to develop instructional activities that might give rise to experientially-based opportunities for children to construct mathematical knowledge. In particular, we used the models to anticipate what might be problematic for children at qualitatively distinct conceptual levels as they interpreted and attempted to solve potential instructional activities. These personally experienced mathematical problems that, we hoped, would arise as the children attempted to achieve their goals in the classroom would constitute opportunities for them to learn (Confrey, 1985; von Glasersfeld, 1987a). In general, the activities were designed to make possible multiple solutions and thus both accommodate individual differences and facilitate sustained small group and whole class discussions about mathematics. Our intent was for children at various conceptual levels to complete the instructional activities in ways that they could explain and justify to others. In this regard, numerous research findings indicate that children enter school with a rich repertoire of conceptually-based self-generated algorithms and problem solving strategies (Baroody, 1987a; Carpenter, Hiebert, & Moser, 1983; Ginsburg, 1977; and Steffe et al., 1983). However, as a consequence of traditional instruction in the early grades, children learn to rely on instrumental procedures at the expense of sense making. Children can follow prescribed rules, but no longer give conceptually-based meaning to what they are doing (Burton, 1984; Ginsburg, 1982; Perry, Church, & Goldin-Meadow, 1988; Ross, 1986). The problem-centered instructional activities were designed to provide learning opportunities in which conceptual and procedural developments would, ideally, go hand in hand (Cobb, Yackel, & Wood, 1988).

In summary, although this approach to mathematics instruction is generally compatible with other child-centered approaches, it differs from typical approaches of this type in two important ways. First, the instructional activities were grounded in detailed analyses of children's mathematical experiences and the processes by which they construct mathematical knowledge. The activities were therefore designed to give rise to opportunities for children to reorganize their mathematical activity and thus develop increasingly sophisticated conceptual understandings. Second, the researchers were primarily responsible for the construction of the instructional activities in consultation with the project teacher. Consequently, the teacher was able to concentrate on the development of her classroom practice and was not distracted by the need to search for or develop from scratch instructional activities that may or may not offer opportunities for children to extend their current mathematical ways of knowing.

Initial Induction of the Project Teacher

As the teacher was to be the researcher/teacher in the experiment, we felt that it was important to help her understand the research-based cognitive models before commencing the classroom teaching experiment (Fennema, Carpenter & Peterson, 1986; Osborne, Bell & Gilbert, 1982; Steffe, 1986). We anticipated that the teacher would change her general view of children's mathematical learning and learn about children's counting types, thinking strategies, and their various conceptions of ten. In the spring prior to the experiment, we met with her once a week to discuss the cognitive models and to watch video-recordings of clinical interviews that had been conducted with her current second-grade students at the beginning of the school year. As we watched the tapes, it became apparent to the project director that although the teacher was taking extensive notes about children's cognitive levels, our conceptual analyses of children's mathematical activity made little sense to her. She seemed to feel "on the spot" whenever we asked about her interpretation of a child's solution and attempted to respond by giving one of the technical labels for a particular conceptual level. The social context we mutually constructed with the teacher during these initial sessions was such that she viewed us as evaluators of her answers. She seemed to ask herself, "What does he want me to say now?" As a consequence, the possibility of attempting to understand the children's mathematical activity did not arise for her. In our view, she was rote learning a list of technical names that would have no relevance to her practice in the classroom. The development of this interaction pattern seemed to be influenced in part by the teacher's view of the project director as a "math professor" who, by definition, knew a lot more than she did. The project director also contributed to the mutual construction of this unproductive context by explaining what he saw in the tapes. This only confirmed the teacher's view of him as an authority who had all the answers.

In an attempt to renegotiate the social norms of their relationship, the project director initiated a dialogue about a topic within the domain of the teacher's expertise—her mathematics textbook. The teacher questioned his suggestion that textbook-based instruction led many children to develop detrimental concepts of place value. The teacher referred to the ability of her students to complete textbook exercises correctly to support her claim that most of them did understand place value. In her view, most of her students were learning the mathematics they were supposed to learn.

In an attempt to make this taken-for-granted assumption about textbook instruction problematic, the project director suggested that she conduct her own interviews with some of her students to ascertain whether his claims were viable or not. She selected two of her better students and video-taped interviews in which she used the same tasks that had been given at the beginning of the school year. A description of these tasks can be found in Cobb and Wheatley (1988). Crucially, the tasks had face validity for the teacher in that successful performance seemed to involve the very concepts she assumed the children had learned as a consequence of her textbook instruction. In the course of the interviews, she began to realize that even though she had carefully taught them the algorithmic procedures specified in the textbook and although they could produce correct answers, neither of the students had reorganized their conceptions of place value since the earlier interviews. In retrospect, we see that our genuine collaboration with the project teacher began when she realized that her current instructional practices were problematic. She now viewed us as people with whom she could work to develop an alternative instructional practice. We had common problems and interests, and could engage in joint pedagogical problem solving.

Reflections on the Induction Process

We learned several important lessons in the course of our interactions with the project teacher. These reflections were of direct relevance to the issue of how to induct other teachers into the project. First, it seemed essential to initiate discussions with teachers on issues about which they considered themselves knowledgeable on the basis of their first-hand experiences. Researchers' formal cognitive models obviously fail to meet this criterion. Second, and relatedly, it became apparent that the project teacher's primary concern was, quite reasonably, the intellectual and social development of her students. The productive phases of her initiation into the project centered on what her students were learning in her classroom during mathematics instruction. Thus, the teacher's classroom served as a learning environment for her even during her induction. From this we later concluded that our interactions with other teachers should focus on specific classroom events that could serve as paradigm cases. Third, the crucial point in our development of a collaborative relationship with the project teacher occurred when she began to realize that her current practice might be problematic. We were then no longer researchers or teachers but people with complementary domains of expertise working on problems of common interest. This strongly indicated to us that our first step when working with other teachers must be to help them become aware of and make problematic aspects of their textbook-based instruction. Only then would they have reason and motivation to attempt to modify their classroom practice while working with us.

The Classroom as an Environment for the Teacher's Learning

When we began the classroom teaching experiment, we still clung to the belief that it would be crucial for the teacher to understand the cognitive models so that she could use them to inform her classroom practice. We assumed that this research-based knowledge would be essential when she analyzed her students' mathematical activity and, more generally, that using the models to guide pedagogical interventions was the hallmark of teaching mathematics in a way compatible with constructivist theory. We therefore expected that the project teacher would draw on detailed inferences she made about each child's thinking as she interacted with the children in small groups and as she orchestrated the whole class discussions. However it became evident to us that she was not applying the formal cognitive models to her practice but instead she was trying to develop her own ways of making sense of her experiences as she interacted with her students. Although the detailed formal models did not appear not to be relevant to the teacher, her practice was compatible with more general aspects of constructivist theory that had been discussed in weekly meetings during her induction into the project. These included the beliefs that children's actions are rational to them and that as teachers we must try to make sense of their meanings (Labinowicz, 1985, 1987).

In the course of analyzing this and other aspects of the teacher's pedagogical actions in the classroom, we assumed that she, like her students, was rational, given her premises. We therefore accepted that she had sound if unarticulate reasons for not attempting to apply the cognitive models to her practice. Once we adopted this stance, we began to realize that researchers construct formal models in contexts that are incompatible with those in which teachers construct the knowledge that informs their practice. Formal models are a product of a series of abstractions and formalizations made by researchers who operate in the context of academic reasoning and attempt to satisfy the current standards of their research community. In contrast, teachers operate in the context of pragmatic pedagogical problem solving in which they have to make on the spot decisions as they interact with their students in specific situations. The distinction between the academic and pragmatic ways of knowing is, in many ways, analogous to that between the principled methods of formal mathematics and the informal, out-of-school mathematics that people construct to resolve the pragmatic mathematical problems they encounter in the course of their everyday lives (cf. Lave, 1988; Rogoff & Lave, 1984).

The Negotiation of Social Norms as an Opportunity to Learn

The teacher's immediate concern at the beginning of the teaching experiment was (in our language) to initiate and guide the mutual construction of classroom social norms that would make it possible for the children to work productively in small groups and express their thinking in whole class discussions. We have argued elsewhere that the processes of negotiating classroom social norms and of negotiating mathematical meanings constitute two distinct levels of discourse (Cobb, Yackel, & Wood, 1988, 1989). The currently established norms form a taken-for-granted framework within which to both engage in mathematical activity and communicate about mathematics.

The teacher appeared to be aware before the teaching experiment began of conflicts between her prior traditional form of practice and classroom norms she now believed were desirable . Her attempts to resolve these conflicts in the context of her practice gave rise to opportunities for her to learn. Further learning opportunities arose for the teacher as she encountered unanticipated problems and made observations that were generally surprising to her. We will discuss both types of learning opportunities first in the whole class setting and then in the small group setting.

Whole Class Interactions

The teacher wanted the children to feel "psychologically safe" to explain how they had actually solved problems when they participated in whole class discussions. However, this conflicted with the traditional teacher elicitation, student response, teacher evaluation pattern that she had been comfortable with. She was concerned that she would be unable to anticipate their responses if she initiated discussions in which the focus was on the children's mathematical activity rather than on an answer or solution method that she had in mind all along. From her perspective, this would create uncertainty and unpredictability in a situation in which she had previously felt in control. Her desire to facilitate and respect children's mathematical thinking was in conflict with her need to maintain control of events in her classroom (Gunstone & Northfield, 1988; Harlen & Osborne, 1985).

Despite her concerns, the teacher began to initiate and guide the renegotiation of social norms in the first mathematics lesson of the school year. This renegotiation was essential in that the expectations she had for the children during whole class discussions were incompatible with the beliefs about their own and the teacher's role that they had constructed in the course of their kindergarten and first grade mathematics instruction (Wood, Cobb, & Yackel, in press).

In particular, the children tacitly assumed that they were expected to figure out the response that the teacher considered appropriate rather than to express their own thinking (Voigt, 1985; Weber, 1986). However, talking about expectations was not enough. If the children were to accept the obligation of making public their mathematical thinking, then the teacher had to accept certain complementary obligations for her own actions. From the children's point of view, a definite risk was involved in attempting to fulfill her expectations. For them, it was one thing to think privately about how to solve a problem, but quite another to express those thoughts to their peers. Their thinking would be subject to public scrutiny and evaluation at the risk of feelings of embarrassment and incompetence. If they were to express their thoughts, then they expected the teacher both to respect their thinking and to place other children under the obligation of doing so. As a consequence, the teacher was obligated not to overtly evaluate their solutions or to try to impose her ways of doing mathematics on them (Cobb, Wood, & Yackel, in press; Wood, in press).

As part of the process of initiating and guiding the renegotiation of classroom norms, the teacher capitalized on particular classroom events by framing them as paradigm cases in which to discuss her expectations with the students. For example, she initiated a discussion about erroneous solutions when some of the children became embarrassed after realizing that their answers were incorrect. In the course of the discussion, she emphasized that sharing such solutions was appropriate in every way in her classroom. More generally, her creative use of paradigm cases enabled her to help the children realize that her primary interest was to understand their solutions and facilitate a dialogue rather than to judge the correctness of their answers. This flexible use of paradigmatic events did not appear to be a consciously applied pedagogical strategy. Rather, it expressed knowledge-in-action that greatly contributed to her effectiveness in achieving a pedagogical agenda compatible with constructivism.

Her fears about losing control of the course of events during whole class discussions were almost immediately alleviated because the children were able to come to a consensus about answers in the very first lesson of the school year without the need for her to steer or funnel the discussions. She also observed that children would frequently revise their thinking in the course of discussions. Thus, renegotiating social norms to make it possible for the students and her to act as a community of validators did not result in an "anything goes" atmosphere. She was fulfilling her obligations as a teacher in that the children did eventually agree on correct answers.

The major surprise that occurred for the teacher as she listened to her students' explanations in whole class discussions was her realization that beginning second graders' mathematical thinking was far more sophisticated than she had previously assumed. She commented, "I have been teaching all this time, and I never knew second graders knew so much about math!" The whole class discussions constituted the first opportunity she had in the course of her teaching career to actually listen to her students as they expressed their mathematical thinking. More generally, her initially surprising observations about her students' capabilities also brought home to her the value of actually listening to what students had to say about mathematics. At the end of the year she commented:

> I have become a better listener. Teachers are basically talkers who feel a strong desire to share their knowledge with other people. Children are no different. If we really make an effort to listen to our students, we will become richer for it.

It was precisely because she learned the importance of listening while interacting with her students in the classroom that she and the students were able to engage in genuine conversations about mathematics. The manner in which she initiated and guided the renegotiation of classroom social norms made this learning possible.

Small Group Interactions

As was the case with whole class discussions, the teacher came to more fully appreciate that her previously taken-for-granted agenda for mathematics instruction was incompatible with mathematical sense making when she initiated the renegotiation of social norms. Her initial concern as she interacted with her students during small group work reflected her assumption that part of her responsibility as a teacher was to constantly monitor her students to ensure that they stayed on task (Maher, 1986). However, she now wanted time to observe and interact with them as they worked in small groups. She was therefore faced with the challenge of initiating and guiding the development of the social norms that would make it possible for the children to work cooperatively without her close supervision as they solved problems and completed the instructional activities (Harlen & Osborne, 1985).

The initial renegotiation of social norms that occurred in the whole class setting was crucial to the development of increasingly productive small group interactions. The children realized that they would be expected to explain and justify how they had solved problems and this facilitated the development of the obligation of making sense of things when they worked in small groups. In addition, the teacher capitalized on events that occurred as the children worked in groups to further discuss her expectations for them. The obligations she attempted to negotiate included respecting each other's thinking, figuring things out for themselves, and working collaboratively to complete the instructional activities. The development of these norms for small group work was facilitated by the use of instructional activities designed to give rise to experientially-based mathematics problems, which in turn generated opportunities for dialogue and communication about mathematics. The instructional activities therefore played a crucial role in making it possible for the small groups to engage in productive mathematical activity. This, together with the renegotiation of social norms, provided an opportunity for the teacher to relinquish her traditional responsibility as an overseer who ensured that the children stayed on task. She commented on several occasions that the children were, for the most part, talking about mathematics as they worked in groups.

Not surprisingly, observations that her students stayed on task as they worked together in a somewhat noisy atmosphere and without the promise of tangible rewards while accepting personally challenging (i.e., hard) problems called into question some of her previous assumptions. To make sense of what she actually saw happening in her classroom, she had to reorganize her beliefs about what motivated her students to engage in mathematical activity. In the process of doing so, she seemed to construct a notion similar to that of task involvement in the achievement motivation literature (Nicholls, 1983, 1989).

For example, she wrote in notes for other teachers:

> Students were motivated to work hard during math time because of the personal satisfaction they felt. Teacher reinforcement was not as necessary as before. I never gave stickers or happy faces for their work and they never asked for those types of rewards either. Further, work that was too easy often meant more behavioral problems. Twenty easy problems were not as self-satisfying as one or two difficult ones.

These comments indicate that doing work was of great importance to the teacher. However, she radically revised her understanding of what it meant to be on task:

> When a child does not appear to be doing any productive thinking, do not be too hasty to judge or criticize the behavior. The student may be reflecting in a non-traditional way which teachers interpret as "goofing off." In reality, . . . this reflection time may be part of thinking through or taking a time-out for a few moments.

The Teacher's Reconceptualization of Her Role

As the whole class and small group social norms necessary for the relatively smooth flow of classroom life became established, the teacher's and children's obligations for their own activity and their expectations for others' activity gradually achieved a fit. In the process, the children began to take increasing responsibility for their own conduct and learning. This did not escape the teacher's attention as she reconceptualized her role:

> The teacher is not the only decision-maker in the classroom. Each student has leadership qualities that can be encouraged. They are responsible for the classroom and its materials. Students can learn a great deal from one another, the teacher is a 'facilitator of learning.' . . .The teacher can set up the physical layout for the room and the students maintain that order—not just the teacher.

This last comment indicates that the teacher seemed to be aware that she and the students together created the classroom social context. The teacher initiated and guided the development of intellectual and social autonomy by negotiating with her students the obligations of explaining and justifying their solutions, resolving conflicts involving solutions and answers, and developing productive small group relationships. It was no longer the teacher's responsibility to provide or sanction the official way to solve problems. Instead, she used her authority to guide and sustain mathematical communication in both whole class and small group settings by listening, offering suggestions, and clarifying children's meanings. In describing the change that took place in her role, she commented:

> My teaching role is pleasantly different. Rather than being the "person with all the answers," the children have been given the opportunity to count on themselves and each other. . . . Giving them responsibilities gives them the feeling that they are needed and are important in our classroom, they do have ownership in what they are learning.

In short, the teacher's reconceptualization of her role went hand in hand with the children's increasing autonomy. Each was made possible by the other and, in the process, mathematics instruction became more "psychically rewarding" (Lortie, 1975) for the teacher. This sustained the teacher's commitment to continue to develop her practice.

Negotiating Mathematical Meanings as an Opportunity to Learn

From the constructivist perspective, learning is an interactive as well as a constructive process (Bruner, 1986; Cobb, in press; von Glasersfeld, 1988). Opportunities for children to construct mathematical knowledge arise as they interact with both the teacher and their peers. As a consequence, their mathematical constructions are not purely arbitrary—anything does not go in the classroom. Instead, their constructions are constrained by an obligation to develop interpretations that fit with those of other members of the classroom community (Bauersfeld, 1988; Blumer, 1969). It is this fit between personal interpretations that makes possible mathematical communication and the subjective experience of a shared, objective mathematical reality (Pierce, 1935; Schutz, 1962; Wittgenstein, 1964). In the course of a mathematical communication, meanings are negotiated and particular mathematical practices are institutionalized and taken for granted as beyond justification by members of the classroom community (Cobb, in press). Mathematics is therefore both an individual constructive activity and a human social activity—a community project (de Millo, Lipton, & Perlis, 1986). The latter aspect of mathematics was most apparent when we focused on the teacher's and children's discussions about mathematics rather than on individual children's construction of mathematical knowledge.

Facilitating Mathematical Learning and Communication

As we have noted, the teacher's primary intention when interacting with her students during both small group and whole class discussions became to facilitate their engagement in meaningful mathematical activity. A major problem began to take shape for the teacher in the course of these interactions. She had concluded during her induction into the project that simply pointing out children's mistakes and telling them what to do did not work. On the other hand, children's mathematical explanations were frequently unacceptable with respect to the institutionalized mathematical practices of the wider community. If direct telling was inappropriate, then so was a blind acceptance of all solutions. The result would be a chaotic "anything goes" in which each child would be allowed to pursue his or her own interests. The teacher gradually developed a form of practice that avoided these twin dangers as she interacted with her students. It is one thing to be non-evaluative during whole class discussions and another to do nothing more than regulate individual children's explanations and ensure that only one child is speaking at a time. The teacher seemed to realize that it was not sufficient for her to regulate the separate explanations of a series of children; she had to foster communication about mathematics among the children and thus make mathematics a community project. This realization was indicated by the manner in which she frequently framed incompatible solutions as problems for the children to resolve. In doing so, she was implicitly communicating to the children her belief that mathematical solutions should be questioned and, when necessary, justified. Thus, she was subtly acculturating the children into her own interpretive stance with regard to mathematical knowledge (Bruner, 1986). This process was most apparent when the teacher encouraged the children to say whether they agreed or disagreed with others' solutions and to settle the ensuing disputes by discussing their reasons.

The teacher experienced greater difficulties in transcending the tension between traditional and *laissez faire* forms of practice when she interacted with the children as they worked in small groups. On one occasion she was working with her weakest student to help him solve a problem that involved tens. The child had been using multilinks arranged in bars of ten. He had been counting individual cubes as he solved the problems. The teacher, in an attempt to help, counted each bar as a unit of ten. After a few minutes of watching, the child told her, "You're confusing me." This made such a strong impression on her that in the subsequent whole class discussion she announced:

> Rick had two sets of multilinks he was adding up. And you know what I did? And I shouldn't have done this, because it kind a confused Rick. I added up all the tens first, and you know what it did to Rick? It confused him. I'm glad he spoke up and said, "I

> can't do it that way." He was counting by ones. I did more to confuse Rick than to help him even though I thought I was [helping him].

In this incident, she openly expressed to the class the tension that she felt between offering suggestions that would help the children solve their mathematical problems and directing them to produce the predetermined response she desired (Voigt, 1985; Wood, Cobb, & Yackel, in press). As the year progressed, she became increasingly sensitive in her interactions with the children and became adept at recognizing when her suggestions were fruitful and when the children merely searched for responses that would fit with her expectations.

The teacher's learning in the classroom illustrates the self-organizing nature of classroom life. It was the teacher who initiated the renegotiation of social norms to allow children to express their mathematical thinking. In the course of listening to their solutions the teacher modified her beliefs about mathematics and extended her understanding of children's learning of mathematics. By drawing on this knowledge, the teacher could better facilitate the children's construction of mathematical knowledge. In doing so, she created further opportunities to listen to creative solutions and thus further elaborated her understanding of second grade mathematics. In a very real sense the teacher and students mutually constructed a social context within which they could learn from each other. Mathematics was a community project. As the teacher and children engaged in and talked about mathematical activity, they created a "microcosm of mathematical culture" (Schoenfeld, 1987). In this setting the children were viewed as having mathematical ideas that were worth knowing. There was a change from the elementary school mathematics tradition of the teacher as the sole validator of official knowledge to one characterized by interaction and the negotiation of mathematical meanings.

Our Current Views on Teacher Development

The project is now in its third year. Thirty second-grade teachers are using the problem-centered instructional activities in their classrooms, twenty-two of them for the second year. Our experiences of interacting with the project teacher who participated in the classroom teaching experiment profoundly influenced the way in which we inducted the other teachers into the project. We first conducted a one-week summer institute with the teachers and then visited their classrooms at least once every two weeks during the first year in which they participated in the project. The teachers also met once a week in small groups to discuss their classroom experiences. In addition, the teachers participated in four after-school working sessions during the school year. Our continued interaction with the teachers throughout the year reflects our belief that classrooms are learning environments for teachers.

The Summer Institute

Our initial goal in the summer institute was to develop situations that would make it possible for the teachers to begin to question their current practices and thus have a reason to consider an alternative approach. In light of our work with the project teacher, we chose children's understanding of place value and their use of the standard two-digit addition algorithm as an initial setting for discussion. This was of immediate interest to the teachers because they considered it a central topic in second grade mathematics and they reported that their students have difficulty in learning to add and subtract with regrouping. We began the week-long session by showing video recordings of children solving textbook and non-textbook tasks. In one of these recordings, children were first shown solving non-textbook tasks which consisted of number sentences such as:

$$22 + 13 = \_\_ \quad \text{and } 16 + 9 = \_\_.$$

The same children were then shown solving addition tasks involving the same number combinations presented in the traditional textbook vertical format. The teachers expected that children who could do the non-textbook tasks would also be able to complete the textbook tasks. Consequently, they were surprised when they found that their assumptions about children's learning were unwarranted. Like the project teacher, they then began to differentiate between correct adherence to accepted procedures and mathematical activity that expressed conceptual understanding.

As the teachers began to question the adequacy of textbook instructional activities and their current ways of teaching, they were willing to consider alternative instructional activities designed to encourage meaningful mathematical activity. In doing so, they demonstrated the value they placed on children's mathematical sense-making. We did not have to convince them that children should learn with understanding. Rather, they had assumed that this kind of learning was occurring in their classrooms. A shared desire to facilitate meaningful learning and a general concern for children's intellectual and social welfare constituted the foundation upon which we and the teachers began to mutually construct a consensual domain. We began to discuss our rationale for an alternative instructional approach by focusing on the crucial role the teacher plays in developing a "problem-solving atmosphere." From our point of view, it was essential that the teachers understand that the instructional activities did not constitute the curriculum. Learning opportunities for the students were not embedded in the activities, but were instead realized as the teachers used the activities in their classrooms while interacting with their students. In the last analysis, it was the teachers' responsibility to initiate and guide the mutual construction of situations conducive to learning. In the course of this discussion with the teachers, we showed video-recorded episodes of small group work and whole class interactions. The teachers frequently asked questions about the pragmatics of the instructional approach and we gave them specific answers about concerns such as techniques for organizing the manipulative materials and using the overhead projector. In addition, we gave relatively direct advice about how to initiate and guide the development of classroom social norms crucial to the establishment of a problem-solving atmosphere (Cobb, Yackel, & Wood, 1988; Cobb, Wood, & Yackel, in press). Our purpose was not to program the teachers to act in a predetermined way but rather, to help them find a way of coping with these concerns as rapidly as possible. In doing so they would have greater opportunity to focus on children's mathematical activity when they used the instructional activities in their classrooms. We were prescriptive to make it possible for classrooms to be learning environments for teachers as well as children (Cobb, Yackel, & Wood, 1988).

In the remainder of the one week institute, the teachers solved mathematical problems in small groups, familiarized themselves with the instructional materials, and visited a simulation of the project classroom. One set of mathematical tasks the teachers solved in groups was created by translating some of the second grade arithmetic activities into base eight (cf. Steffe, 1987). In the course of completing these activities and discussing their solutions, the teachers appeared to appreciate further that computational tasks can be solved in multiple ways. We also discussed the similarity between the teachers' solution methods and the children's methods that had been viewed earlier in the week. Finally, we asked the teachers to reflect on the difficulties that they experienced when constructing eight as a unit. Our hope was that they would begin to question the apparent obviousness of base ten numeration and begin to appreciate the intellectual challenge that second graders have to cope with.

During their first visit to the project classroom, teachers observed a demonstration mathematics lesson conducted by the initial project teacher with those of her students who were available to participate during their summer vacation. After the demonstration, we discussed the teachers' questions about and interpretations of classroom events. The next day the children returned to the classroom and the teachers worked with an individual child to investigate his or her mathematical interpretations and solutions. Again a discussion followed in which the teachers shared their observations. The teachers' comments indicated that they were learning about children's ways of solving mathematical problems and beginning to become aware of limitations in their understanding of their own students' mathematical thinking. As this brief discussion of the summer institute makes clear, we attempted to develop situations in which the teachers could engage in experientially based problem solving relevant to their practice. In general, we have come to believe that attempts to influence teachers knowledge and beliefs will not be at their most effective unless they draw on teachers' first-hand experiences of interacting with their students during mathematics instruction (Bush, 1986; Carpenter & Fennema, 1988; Cooney, 1985). For this reason, we did not discuss formal models of early number development during the summer institute.

The School Year

At the beginning of the school year, we discussed the potential value of the teachers meeting once a week in small groups at their school to discuss problems, concerns, and insights. A member of the project staff visited their classrooms each week at the beginning of the school year and then gradually decreased the frequency of visits to once every two weeks for the remainder of the year. The primary purposes of the visits were to address teachers' pragmatic concerns (e.g., how to involve all children in discussions) and to help them make problematic certain aspects of their practice that were outside their awareness (e.g., responding to children's solutions in an evaluative if subtle manner). During these visits, we encouraged the teachers to think through problems themselves rather than to rely on us to tell them what to do (see Cobb, Yackel, & Wood, 1988, for a more detailed discussion). Consequently, we had intellectual autonomy as a developmental goal for them as well as for their students. There were two indications of having had some success in this regard: (1) the manner in which the teachers increasingly relied on their own judgments when selecting from the many instructional activities and materials, and (2) the decisions by which teachers determined activities to focus upon during class instruction.

Within the first few weeks of the school year, the teachers encountered difficulties when they attempted to interpret their students' mathematical solutions. Some specifically requested assistance in judging the relative sophistication of particular children's mathematical solutions. It was at this point that the teachers began to appreciate the relevance of relatively detailed knowledge of children's mathematical cognitions to their practice. We therefore conducted a series of working sessions that focused on various methods children use as they attempt to solve arithmetical problems. Initial sessions dealt with counting by ones and thinking strategies, and later sessions with units of ten, non-standard computational algorithms, and multiplicative and divisional concepts. These sessions were designed to dovetail with the instructional activities the teachers were using in their classrooms. Our purpose in orchestrating the discussions was to encourage the teachers to construct mutually acceptable interpretations of a particular child's solution. Although we asked questions and drew attention to aspects of a solution that contradicted particular interpretations, we did not attempt to steer the teachers to an interpretation in terms of the formal cognitive models. Nor did we share our technical vocabulary with them; it was not relevant to their purposes. We thus attempted to walk the pedagogical tightrope as we interacted with the teachers in much the same way that we hoped they would when interacting with their students during mathematics instruction. This was one of the fundamental lessons we learned when interacting with the project teacher. More generally, we became aware of the hypocrisy involved in failing to apply our developing conceptions of the learning-teaching process reflectively to guide our own practice. We, like the teachers, encountered problematic and surprising situations that challenged us to question some of our taken-for-granted assumptions. Both our own and the teachers' pedagogical knowledge and beliefs developed as we struggled with the problems of practice.

Beliefs and Practice

We can clarify the way we currently work with teachers by relating it to two alternative approaches. One approach assumes that a change in teachers beliefs will lead to specific changes in classroom practices which, in turn, will result in improved student learning. In other words, changes in beliefs are assumed to come before changes in practice. An extreme example of this approach would be to conduct intensive workshops with teachers and then to leave them to their own devices to figure out what it might mean for their practice. Guskey (1986) observed that "current research on teacher change indicates that the assumptions of this model may be inaccurate, at least under the specific conditions of staff development for experienced teachers" (p. 6).

Although we do not subscribe to this approach, Guskey's outright dismissal seems overly hasty. We did attempt to influence teachers beliefs during the summer institute. We devised situations in which they could draw on their first-hand experiences to question the beliefs that their students were learning with understanding, that there is typically one way to solve second grade mathematics tasks, and that certain conceptual developments such as constructing an understanding of place value numeration ought to be relatively simple even if students do experience difficulties. In doing so, we encouraged the teachers to make aspects of their current practice problematic. In effect, we asked the teachers to reconsider what they thought they knew. Only then would they have both an initial awareness of other possibilities and reason and motivation to pursue these possibilities by developing a new form of practice.

Guskey proposed a second approach to teacher development that is premised on the assumption that "significant changes in teachers' beliefs and attitudes are likely to take place only after changes in student learning outcomes are evidenced" (p. 7). This assumption led Guskey to argue that "change is a learning process for teachers that is developmental and primarily experientially based" (p. 7). It follows that since "change occurs mainly after implementation takes place and evidence of improved student learning is gained, it is continued support following the initial training that is most crucial" (p. 10). This is because "no matter how much advanced staff development occurs, it is when teachers try to implement the new approach that they have the most specific concerns and doubts" (p. 10).

We will consider Guskey's approach in some detail because it is easy to jump to the conclusion that it is highly compatible with the way we attempt to work with teachers. First, Guskey dismisses the value of gaining an initial sense of commitment from teachers. In contrast, our experience indicates the importance of helping teachers develop personal, experientially-based reasons and motivations for reorganizing their classroom practice. Second, he seems to view a new form of practice as a collection of "concrete and practical ideas" (p. 6) devised by researchers or staff developers and then given ready-made to teachers. He suggests, for example, that "to be effective a staff development program must offer teachers practical ideas that can be efficiently used to directly enhance desired student learning outcomes" (p. 6).

Further, "if a staff development effort is to be successful, it must clearly illustrate how the new practices can be implemented" (p. 9). The emphasis seems to be on ensuring that teachers teach in the way the staff developer thinks they should rather than on helping them develop a new form of practice. In short, the staff developer is an authority rather than a collaborator when it comes to pedagogical issues. To be sure, we were relatively directive once the teachers began to see their current form of practice as problematic. But this was to make it possible for them to learn in their classrooms rather than to ensure that they taught the way we wanted them to. Third, although Guskey acknowledges that "teachers' knowledge of teaching is validated very pragmatically" (p. 7), he takes this to mean that they focus solely on learning outcomes. There seems to be no room for the possibility that teachers will reflect on what they are doing and develop a rationalization for their activity. Instead, they merely check to see if what they have been told to do works. In fact, Guskey believes it essential that staff developers "ensure that teachers receive regular feedback on student learning progress" (p. 9). Apparently, teachers do not attempt to interpret students' thinking and learning in the course of their classroom interactions but instead rely on outcome measures of one sort or another. Our experience directly contradicts this assumption. Finally, the very notion of what constitutes a desirable learning outcome seems beyond question in Guskey's approach. In contrast, the issue of what should be our goals as mathematics educators was addressed repeatedly in our discussions with teachers. Is it improved test scores and more correct answers, or are we more concerned that students become increasingly autonomous and task-involved as they engage in meaningful mathematical activity?

In general, our primary goal when working with teachers has been to help them develop forms of practice that they can justify. In doing so, we have attempted to encourage teacher autonomy (Kamii, 1985). This, we believe, is the key to whatever success we have had in initiating and guiding relatively radical reorganizations in both teachers' beliefs and their classroom practices. It is perhaps because Guskey's approach encourages teachers to view themselves as recipients of researchers' wisdom that he is led to assert that teachers generally oppose radical alterations to their present instructional procedures:

> Programs or innovations that are dramatically different from teachers' current practices or that require teachers to make major revisions in the way they presently teach are unlikely to be implemented well, if at all. (p. 9)

In presenting the rationale for his approach, Guskey challenged the assumption that changes in practices follow changes in beliefs and instead suggests that beliefs depend on practice. We have difficulty with both contentions in that they are premised on the underlying assumption that the relationship between beliefs and practices is one of linear causality. In our view, arguments about the direction of the assumed causality miss the point; the very nature of the relationship needs to be reconceptualized. Our current work with teachers is based on the alternative assumption that beliefs and practice are dialectically related. Beliefs are expressed in practice, and problems or surprises encountered in practice give rise to opportunities to reorganize beliefs. For example, we argued when analyzing the project teacher's learning that her beliefs and practices were interdependent and developed together. And it is precisely because of this interdependency that her classroom was her primary learning environment.

Conclusion

Throughout this chapter, we have attempted to demonstrate that teachers and students mutually constructed the social contexts within which to learn from each other. At another level, we and the teachers mutually constructed a social context in the course of our interactions that made it possible for us to learn from them and vice versa. In the course of these interactions, we radically revised our beliefs about how we could help teachers reorganize their practice. At the outset of the project, we took for granted the goal of attempting to transform the teachers into constructivists who thought just like we did. It was only when working with teachers that we became aware of the gross hypocrisy implicit in this goal. Clearly, our tolerance for a diversity of ideas did not extend to our epistemology.

Our goal, as we now see it, is to help teachers develop forms of pedagogical practice that improve the quality of their students' mathematical education, not to spread a particular philosophical doctrine. We are well aware that there are significant differences in the ways we and the teachers rationalize during their mathematics instruction. Few, if any, of the teachers would agree completely with a statement such as "learning is the process by which students reorganize their sensory-motor and conceptual activity to resolve experientially-based problematic situations" even if they could unravel the terminology. The crucial point is that our own and the teachers' interpretations of classroom events need only be compatible for the purposes at hand. We have learned to discuss differences between our own and teachers' interpretations only if they are differences that make a difference in terms of classroom practice. In this regard, we agree with Kilpatrick's (1987) contention that there is not a one-to-one correspondence between background theories and forms of pedagogical practice. It is, in fact, for this reason that we speak of "forms of teaching compatible with constructivism" rather than "constructivist teaching."

Chapter 10: Teacher Development in Mathematics in a Constructivist Framework

Carolyn A. Maher and Alice Alston

Rutgers University

> In what I have said I have taken for granted the soundness of the principle that education in order to accomplish its ends both for the individual learner and for society must be based upon experience—which is always the actual life-experience of some individual. (Dewey, 1938, p. 89)

Only decades ago John Dewey argued for a carefully developed philosophy of experience. Yet the sources of a contructivist approach to learning have been shown to span a long history of over 2500 years (von Glasersfeld, Chapter 2, this volume). As recently as five years ago, intense debate regarding the credibility of a "constructivist approach" to mathematics learning extended in some way to involve members of the mathematics education community. In 1986, Brophy and Confrey publicly debated the implications of the approach at an intense AERA session. At the 1987 Psychology of Mathematics Education meeting in Montreal, plenary speakers argued for or against the appropriateness of the perspective as a framework for research in mathematics education. Members of the community struggled to make sense of the philosophical and practical issues involved. For many mathematics educators, the customary assumption that each student was building up in his or her own mind a good (if not yet complete) replica of the ideas in the teacher's mind had rather suddenly come into question. The methodological issues became more compelling as mounting evidence indicated the presence of many student misconceptions about mathematical ideas that previously had been overlooked. Surely the constructions by students were very much influenced by the nature of the "activity " that was taking place in mathematics classroom environments. It was not easy to dismiss the debate. By reconsidering the nature of student experience in the classroom, methodological and pedagogical issues engaged members of the community in a reconsideration of their personal perspectives and an examination of the implications of a constructivist view on learning.

The suggestion by Noddings (Chapter 1, this volume) that constructivism is not a strong epistemological position and might better be considered a post-epistemological perspective makes possible a reconciliation that, while not resolving a basic point of difference, enables mathematics educators to get on with their business of finding ways to help teachers learn to provide environments for children that will foster powerful mathematical constructions. Noddings calls our attention to the "power of the environment to press for adaptation, the temporality of knowledge and the existence of multiple selves behaving in consonance with rules of various subcultures" (Chapter 1, this volume, p. 12). This perspective seems to be in accord with von Glasersfeld's views, as well as of his interpretations of Piaget, concerning the way knowledge is actively built by the cognizing subject and how the function of cognition is adaptive in terms serving to organize and make sense of the experience of the subject (von Glasersfeld, Chapter 2, this volume). Whether or not one's construction represents something that is beyond the experience of an individual, that is, representing according to von Glasersfeld, a state or feature of an experience/independent world, will not be pursued here. For our purposes, suffice it to say, that there are powerful ways of reasoning about mathematical ideas, concepts, and procedures that can be built by teachers and students in environments designed to facilitate such constructions (Maher, 1986). The perspective of constructivism provided by von Glasersfeld as a *theory of knowing* rather than a *theory of knowledge* emphasizes the importance of the establishment of environments (in this case mathematical and social) in which students have opportunity to connect their everyday experience and conceptual practice so that these become useful in their daily living.

The educational philosophy that has now come to be referred to as "constructivism" has been the basis for extensive and ongoing work in mathematics teacher development in New Jersey. It is consistent with Dewey's "experiential education" and has implications for work with teachers and their students. For teachers, this means personal experience in several, often interacting, domains: in their making sense of the mathematics by actively building mathematics and what it means to think mathematically (from the perspective described by Davis & Maher , Chapter 5 this volume); experiences in studying children and how children think mathematically; experience in designing better classroom explorations and experiences for children, and a thoughtful re-appraisal of what "mathematics" really is and what sorts of "evaluation" we really need.

The extensive ongoing work in New Jersey schools has provided careful observations of teachers engaged in experiences intended to empower them to teach mathematics from the perspective of encouraging and guiding children in their constructive endeavors of building systems of representations. From this work we have found that teachers, like children, learn in social contexts in which they can interact and make sense of their experiences (see, also,Cobb, Wood, & Yackel, Chapter 9, this volume).

Theoretical Perspective

The New Jersey work is derived from a constructivist perspective on learning. It rests on the view that learning is contingent upon the activity and involvement of the learner. Piaget, in his early theory of knowledge, stressed the notion of the subject's active construction in learning mathematics, noting:

> Mathematics is, first of all and most importantly, actions exercised on things, and the operations themselves are more actions, but well coordinated among themselves and only imagined instead of being materially executed. Without a doubt it is necessary to reach abstraction, and this is even natural in all areas during the mental development of adolescence, but abstraction is only a sort of trickery and deflection of the mind if it doesn't constitute the crowning stage of a series of previously uninterrupted concrete actions (Piaget, 1948, p. 103).

This idea of knowledge being built up by a subject's well coordinated actions on things in trying to make sense of experiences is central to a constructivist position. The notion, in perhaps another form, is offered by Davis (1984, 1985a, 1985b, 1987, 1989) who gives us a description for learning mathematics as the building-up in one's mind of certain "powerful symbol systems" to represent mathematical situations. Steffe (Chapter 11, this volume) describes mathematical learning as the development of an "encompassing network" of mathematical knowledge. Lawler (in press) uses the notion of "bricolage," a term derived from Levi Strauss in describing "the concrete thought of not-yet-civilized people," in providing an image for the self-constructive processes of the mind. He thereby offers a framework from which to view the uniqueness of individuals, each of whom makes sense of the world by means of a personal history of conceptions and appreciations of situations. In his observations of his daughter, Miriam, Lawler shows that what made sense to her was dominant over what she was told. Observations of Ling Chen (Davis & Maher, Chapter 5, this volume) and Brian and Scott (Maher & Davis, Chapter 6, this volume) provide further support to the notion that what is durable for the learner is what makes sense. One implication for a constructivist theory of knowledge, according to Confrey (Chapter 8, this volume), is that students are continually constructing understandings of their experiences.

The Nature of Experience for Teachers

Kidder (1989) demonstrates that teachers also learn from experience:

> Like everyone else, teachers learn through experience, but they learn without much guidance. One problem,of course, is that experience, especially the kind that is both repetitious and disappointing, can easily harden into narrow pedagogical theories. (p. 51)

As an example, Kidder suggest the following:

> Most schools have a teacher with a theory built on grudges. This teacher knows that there is just one way to conduct a lesson; she blames the children and their parents if the children don't catch on; she has a list of types and makes her students fit them; and she prides herself on her realism—most children come to school, she knows, to give

> her a hard time. Current research holds that most teachers get set in their ways, both their good and bad ones, after about four years of learning by experience. (p. 51)

Teachers, confined to their own classrooms often are trapped in narrow, isolated and repetitive environments in which experiences and responses to them are predictably guided by the models created by them earlier in similar environments. Confrey (Chapter 8, this volume) gives an example of a teacher whose models of a student's mathematical thinking are built upon attention to the student's interpretations and strategies. At issue, then, is how this kind of teaching can be developed—what kind of environments are appropriate for teachers so that their experiences can be extended and enriched and thus cause the narrow cycle to be interrupted and consequently rebuilt?

Clearly, new environments are needed that make possible opportunities for building "more powerful" constructions. Situations are needed which enable teachers as learners to extend their knowledge and to interact with others in the social negotiation of meanings derived from these experiences to provide opportunity for continued growth. The notion that ideas are built-up by the (teacher) learner and can be developed further by rich experience and the social interactions that take place with others.is gaining more attention (e.g., see Cobb, Wood, & Yackel, Chapter 11, this volume; Lawler, in press). Common among these views is the notion that learning mathematics occurs over a period of time as a learner is actively engaged in building up systems of cognitive representations and making connections among them. An important foundation for constructing even more complex systems of knowledge about teaching includes the building of systems of knowledge about the following:

1. How children interpret the ideas in school mathematics;
2. What kinds of strategies children invent and use; and
3. How to interpret the kinds of errors children make.

Attention to these behaviors better enables the teacher to aid the student in building more powerful constructions.

The New Jersey Projects

Observations of teachers in our projects have provided some insight into how they build-up their own systems of representations of mathematical ideas, as well as how they become more attentive to children's mathematical thinking. In this paper, we focus on two kinds of experiences for teachers.

The first is one in which teachers are engaged in a mathematical exploration. By *doing* mathematics, they have an opportunity to become more *aware* of their own mathematical thinking as they work to build greater understanding of some mathematical ideas. As they engage in their own problem solving, opportunities naturally evolve in which they become more aware of their personal approaches and begin to consider the *implications* of this experience for the learning of their *students*.

The second is an episode in which a teacher is conducting a task-based interview with a student. This experience is analyzed in terms of the teacher's attention to the child's mathematical thinking. Both have implications for teacher preparation and development.

Teachers Doing Mathematics

In the following example a group of teachers was seated around a table containing a variety of materials: trading chips, pattern blocks, and squared materials. Using materials of their choice, the teachers were asked to construct and justify their solutions to the following problem taken from Lesh and Zawojewski (1987):

> Two jars were sitting on a table in a classroom. One contained 1000 blue beads and the other contained 500 yellow beads. The teacher took 20 beads out of the blue bead jar and put them into the yellow bead jar. After shaking that jar until the yellow and blue beads were thoroughly mixed, she randomly selected 20 beads from the mixed jar and put them into the jar of blue beads. After she finished, were there more blue beads in the yellow bead jar than there were yellow beads in the blue bead jar? (p. 43).

Transcriptions from videotapes illustrate some of the approaches, considerations, and solution paths that occurred. Five teachers—Carol, Fran, Kathy, Ron, and Susie—after quietly reading and thinking alone about the problem, began to talk about their ideas.

K: Let's draw a picture. That's how we did the last time.

R: You don't know how many. They may be mixed. More blue in the yellow or yellow in the blue.

S: Going over you're getting pure blue; but going back, you're not getting pure yellow, you're getting mixed.

R: How to prove it?

S: I don't know. Unless it's probability. You know—how many chances that you'd get a blue.

R: There would be more yellow. There are 500 yellow.

S: But you're only taking 20. The best you could do would be even. It's either equal—or more blue—or more yellow. It was pure blue going in and you shake them up.

R: The possibility—probability—whatever—is there would be more yellow. Shake them up—500—the probability is there would be more yellow.

S: You can only have 20 blues in the yellow jar at most. Let's act it out. [She then reached over to get chips.]

R: It's too many. Let's let them represent.

K: One per hundred.

S: That's 5 yellows?

F: Five yellows and 10 blues. [She counted them out.]

S: [Staring at the chips] It won't work. Let's use more.

[The five teachers began counting out chips, talking as they did about topics unrelated to the problem.]

S: Kathy suggested that we should use 100 blues. That will be 10 each.

[Fran began counting and stacking blue chips in piles of 10. Susie, Kathy, and Beth all began stacking yellows. Kathy made 3 piles of 10 and Beth made 3 piles of 10.]

R: There's 50 [blues] there. [He pointed to Fran's 5 stacks.]

[All of the blue chips had been used. Susie, then, placed some red and green chips on the table.]

S: Let's use anything except yellow.

[Susie, Ron, and Kathy worked together and added 4 more stacks.]

K: Now there are 90 [blue chips, along with some reds and greens].

R: We need one more stack. [He added one more stack, using 100 chips in 10 stacks to represent 1000 blue chips.]

[Susie observed while doing this activity how it could be appropriate for children's learning.]

S: Kids could get a real sense with this of how much a stack of 10 really is.

[Beth then added 2 of her stacks of yellow chips to Kathy's 3 stacks. Susie removed the extra yellow chips, leaving the 5 stacks, totalling 50 yellow chips, to represent 500.]

R: OK. We're all set. Now take 20 out of here. [He reached for 2 stacks of blues.]

S: No ... 2.

R: Oh! [He hesitated and looked at all of the chips, then replaced the two stacks and took 2 single chips.] ... 2.

K: So ... shake 'em baby!

R: OK—Put them in with all of these. [He held up the plastic bag and the others filled it with all 50 of the yellow chips and the 2 blue chips.] Now shake! [He shook the bag vigorously.] We must be random now.

[Ron then closed his eyes, reached in, and took out 2 chips. The two that he chose happened to be yellow.]

S: There's more yellow. No ... it's the same.

B: But how do you explain?

S: It's the same now, But what are the odds? There's the best chance that there will be more blues in the yellow jar because you're always taking 20 blues over. You're always taking blues over—never yellows.

R: It's the same because of the way we picked. We could have picked both blue—or 10 and 10.

S: Then it would still be the same. [She began to write down some numbers.] How about 18 blue? No, 19? Then there would be 1 blue and 1 yellow. It will always be the same!

F: But it has to be at random.

S: Then let's make a table of random. It won't be the same proportion because there are more blues.

K: But how can you set this up as a pattern?

S: We'll make a table. Or do we need a formula?

F: Do you think that kids would make a table?

R: Yeah [answering Susie] . It has to equal 20 every time.

Notice that after the teachers created a simpler problem, they connected it to the original one by choosing numbers of chips that were proportional to those in the problem. Susie's monitoring of Ron was accepted quite naturally as he adjusted his choice of the number of blue chips to be added to the bag from two stacks, or 20 chips, to two chips, each of which represented 10 blue chips. Notice also that all five teachers were participating to some extent in both the discussion and the construction of the model.

After considering the possibility of solving the problem using probability, the teachers decided to build a solution by charting the possible events in a table. As they began to carry out this strategy, the question of an alternative "rule" that might be applied was raised, considered, and then integrated into the solution as a description of the mathematics of the problem.

S: At one end all 20 come back; there are no blues in the yellow and no yellows in the blue. At the other end none of those like our sample—20 blues here and 20 yellows here.

[Beth and Susie became engaged in discussion as to how this experience could have relevance to their teaching.]

B: But how do you use this?

S: I use this kind of thing every week ... when we've finished a test or something. I tried to get the children to do them [problems] at home, but that didn't work so now I have them do it together during class.

[The teachers appeared to agree on the conclusion that there would always be the same number. They continued to consider how they might justify their solution.]

S: It doesn't matter how many there are in all. That's extra information.

The group then counted out exactly 20 of each color and began to record as they acted out each possible case of moving and returning 20 beads from one jar to the other. Kathy, in attempting to generalize her observations, was questioned by Ron who, trying to make sense of what she was doing, seemed to interpret her statement as a formula. Notice Fran's (and Susie's) immediate response.

S: In this jar there have to be 20 minus the number of blues going to the other jar ... gives you the blues left in the yellow far. 10 - 19 - 18 - 17 - It's going to be the same.

K: It's gotta be the same; 20 minus Y plus or minus; it's B plus Y equals 20 and 20 minus Y equals B. No?

S: You're right.

R: A formula?

S: No.

F: A table.

It is interesting to observe how naturally the teachers moved from their role as problem solvers and became engaged in reflection about their own problem-solving behavior. Some indicated awareness of the strategies used and unsuccessful solution paths pursued. Some began to estimate how students of different ages might solve the problem.

S: What we're doing is modeling. That makes sense to me. They're a complement. They add up to 20. It's something about equality ... like a scale. No matter where you put the 20, they're going to be there.

B: It will be the same. The probability is that you're going to take out a lot of yellows, but it will be the same.

S: My initial reaction was wrong. I thought there would have to be more blues. I forgot whatever blues come out, they have to be balanced. There might be a formula?

R: That would make it more difficult.

S: Kids could do a table.

R: Higher grades might make a formula.

S: We made a scale model. First low, then worked up, then just showing 20.

[At this point, conversation among group members shifted to casual discussions with each other. The camera continued to operate and we were fortunate to capture Susie's comment about the value of this kind of learning for children and also for herself.]

S: Give them a problem. Let them model with rods or pattern blocks or whatever and then record it on graph paper. I tell you, I never learned it—I never learned the theory of it—like division of fractions. It was just the opposite of multiplication—I just wrote it down and flipped it over. Now I can see how you divide and it gets bigger. After they do it they should put up solutions and share them. That's better than you doing it.

The workshop leader (L) reconvened the entire group of teachers for purposes of sharing with each other what had occurred in the smaller groups. The leader asked them how they had gone about solving the problem. Susie was first to respond. We think it is important to recall the consistency of her introspection and reflection about learning and teaching which was indicated in the previous analysis. We see her now comfortable and eager to share her group's activities with the entire group.

S: I thought there would be more blues in the yellow jar. They thought there would definitely be more yellows in the blue far. We came to a compromise. We did a table and found it was the same. We couldn't put it into a formula: 19 - 19 - 18 - 18. They were complements.

Willie, from a second group, reported their approach.:

W: The numbers were too large. We reduced them because we couldn't conceptualize it.

L: How could you be sure that you could do that?

W: Because the concept was the same.

The leader then asked the group whether there might be conditions that would cause the numbers in the two jars to be different. Anita, from a third group, responded.

A: [It happens] if you take out less or more than you put back. We tried each, and sometimes there were more and sometimes less.

Susie's response indicated continued reflection, while Anita raised an issue about use of language.

S: There were lots of distracting things in the problem—like probability—and things that I used to know [about mathematics].

A: Yes. That word "than." What was the question really asking?

S: My kids would say it had to be one or the other—not think that it could be the same.

Merle, a member of a fourth group of teachers, expressed concern about her students in light of her own experience. Here, we see Anita responding to Merle.

M: I found it difficult to keep the question in mind as I worked on the problem. How do you help children do this?

A: We bring things [that we know] that confuse us.

M: They don't understand the question, if it is worded different from something that they have done.

L: What if you really did the problem with jars of beads?

M: That would be good—but then how do you relate the real situation to a verbal problem?

L: Those are the questions that we are addressing in this project.

The kinds of mathematical behaviors and social interactions that are indicated in the episode described here are what we value and hope teachers will strive for in their mathematics teaching. We believe that experiences such as these are a necessary component for further building and extending a teacher's conceptual framework about learning and teaching mathematics and are necessary for orchestrating similar environments for children

Teachers Paying Attention to Children's Thinking

In our work, task-based interviews have been useful in directing teachers' attention to children's thinking. In preparation for the interview experience, teachers first observe videotapes of children doing mathematics, both in small groups as a part of regular classroom instruction and individually, in task-based interviews. The interview format calls for attention to the process of the child's problem-solving behavior, various representations that are built, and how the child connects them.

We use an example of an interview about fractions that was analyzed from the perspective of the child's thinking (Davis & Maher, Chapter 5, this volume, pp. 74-76). Our attention, in this chapter, is on the teacher-interviewer, Regina, as she works to build a model of the child's understanding. The child, Ling Chen, had just completed fifth-grade and was given three problems to solve about fractions. Although each problem involved the numbers 1/3 and 1/2 and resulted in an answer of 1/6, the structure of each problem was different. The first problem that Regina posed for Ling Chen was as follows:

Compare 1/3 and 1/2. Which fraction is larger, and by how much?

Ling Chen answered these questions correctly on the basis of models that she built, first, with rubber bands on a geoboard; second, with a drawing; and finally using pattern blocks. In each construction, she superimposed 1/3 of the amount onto 1/2 of the amount and figured out the difference.

Regina then asked Ling to use the numbers 1/2 and 1/3 and their difference (which Ling had said was 1/6) in a story problem. Ling made up and wrote the following problem:

Karen had a whole candy bar. She gave 1/2 to Kathy and 1/3 to Paul. How much does she have left?

Regina began by asking Ling Chen to read the problem aloud and then to solve it. Ling spontaneously built a model of her solution using Pattern Blocks. She used one yellow hexagon to represent a whole candy bar, one red trapezoid to represent Kathy's half and one blue parallelogram for Paul's third. Regina acknowledged her solution and asked her to record it, and then to solve it numerically.

R: I see your model. Can you draw a picture for me?

[Ling then drew a picture of what she had built.]

R: Very nice. I wonder if we can solve that using numbers now.

[Ling solved the problem numerically by changing 1/3 and 1/2 to equivalent fractions with a common denominator, adding to obtain 5/6, and subtracting 5/6 from 1 (which she renamed as 6/6) to get 1/6 as an answer.]

Regina then directed Ling's attention to the possibility of recognizing connections among her representations.

R: That was some problem! Now just let me make sure what you're doing—and maybe we can explain with these (the blocks that were a part of the model). We had the 1/3 [she points to the 1/3 in the numerical solution]. Whose was that?

L: Paul's. [She moves the blue parallelogram forward.]

R: ...and then the 1/2?

L: That was Kathy's. [She moves the red trapezoid forward.]

R: Your answer says 5/6. I don't see 5/6.

L: You have to show with the green. [She covers the trapezoid with 3 green triangles and the parallelogram with 2 triangles.]

R: In your story, what happened to those 5/6?

L: They were given to people.

R: So—who got what?

Ling pointed again to each part of the model and indicated that 3/6 was for Kathy, and 2/6 was for Paul .

R: And who gets this? [Pointing to the final answer of 1/6.]

L: That's Karen's. [She pulls forward the remaining green triangle.]

Regina , satisfied with Ling Chen's explanation, continued the interview by asking Ling to read aloud and then solve a third problem:

Jane has 1/3 of a candy bar. She gives 1/2 of what she has to Mike. How much of the candy bar does she give to Mike?

Again Ling Chen spontaneously built a model of her problem solution and then explained what she had built. In response to Regina's request to record her answer, Ling wrote 1/6. Regina then continued:

R: You showed me what you did there. Can you draw that for me again so I'll remember it? [Ling begins to draw.] You can trace the blocks if you like.

Ling, having drawn and labelled each part of the solution, proceeded to explain it to Regina, pointing to each part of the solution as she talked.

L: This is Jane's 1/3, and she gives 1/2 of it to Mike. This is Mike's. This is Jane's half, what Jane has left. See ... 1/6 [Taking green triangles and placing them on her model.] Six of these would make the candy bar. It's also half of the 1/3.

Regina seemed to continue pursuing Ling Chen's understanding of the representation she built.

R: This blue represented is 1/3? Because why?

L: Because she had 1/3 of a candy bar.

R: Refresh my memory. How do I know that is 1/3?

L: Because three make the candy bar. [She spontaneously built a "candy bar" from 3 parallelograms to illustrate.]

Regina continued the interview asking for a solution with numbers. We think it is important to note that Regina accepted Ling's solutions without comment. Neither her tone nor her facial expression appeared to be judgmental.

R: Oh. I see now. That's pretty neat. You answered the problem. You used the blocks to do it—and you used a picture to do it. Can you do that problem with numbers?

When Ling divided 1/3 by 1/2 and got 2/3 for an answer, Regina made no comment (see Davis & Maher, Chapter 5, this volume).

L: I must have done it wrong. Dividing fractions isn't my thing.

R: Blocks are your thing? [softly laughing] Which answer do you believe?

L: I believe it's 1/6.

R: You believe that it is 1/6?

L: Yes. Maybe I did it ... maybe I should have done it this way.

Regina watched, smiling and noncommital, as Ling divided 1/2 by 1/3 and got 3/2 for a second answer.

L: That's not right either.

Regina continued in her effort to estimate which of Ling Chen's representations was dominant.

R: Hmm. Now you've got 3 answers here. Which do you believe?

L: Still 1/6.

R: Still believe it's 1/6?

L: It should be like this [pointing to the first written division calculation].

R: Hmm. [She listens without expressing agreement or disagreement.]

L: ... but it doesn't. I don't know how. Let's see. Oh!

[Ling writes 1/3 divided by 1/2 equals 1/3 times 1/2 or 1/6.]

L: I should have multiplied these two numbers because these two numbers add up whatever go together to make 1/6.

Regina still made no comment about Ling's solutions to the problem. (The interview was conducted in a school setting and the signal of the bell indicated that Regina's time with Ling Chen must come to a close.) Before Regina terminated the interview she asked Ling Chen to discriminate between the structures of two of the three problems.

R: You've done two problems here. This one and the one you made up. How are these problems alike and how are they different?

L: They're alike because both gave something away. They're different because Karen gave something to two people and Jane only gave to one. Karen had a whole candy bar and Jane only had 1/3 of a candy bar and they gave different amounts to people.

The episode presented here describes how one teacher, Regina, was initiated into an experience that provided opportunity to pay attention to and understand a child's mathematical thinking. The opportunity was extended as Regina reviewed the tape with her partner, and discussed and shared the episode with the other teachers. The initial activity led to a more detailed analysis of Ling's efforts to reconcile her concrete and symbolic representations as the tape was reviewed with staff and other participating teachers The process of planning, carrying out, reviewing and sharing such experiences has been an effective component of teacher development work in New Jersey .

Implications for Classroom Teaching

In our work we have seen issues emerge for teachers as they begin to carry out classroom activities which lead to further reflection about children's understanding, how problem tasks should be refined for future use, and what should happen next. What we have observed is that teachers begin to pay increased attention to children's thinking. Initially, teachers express concern about developing activities that would engage the children in explorations that could facilitate the building of particular concepts, under the assumption that the strategies used by children would follow the order determined by the curriculum. Teachers soon discover that children are interested in the activities, and are naturally motivated by the creative possibilities of constructing their own models to fill the requirements of each problem. For some students this provides a freedom to discover or invent procedures and to consider different ways to build solutions not necessarily according to the plans predetermined by the teacher. As teachers begin to look in finer detail at their students' mathematical thinking, more attention is given to selecting activities that help them better understand children's ideas and identify possible misconceptions. Assessment of the effectiveness of a lesson leads to revisions that now could be made based on estimates of the quality of individual students' learning.

A second set of issues addressed by teachers deals with classroom organization and the teacher's role in carrying out the lessons. In their first attempts at using this kind of activity, teachers frequently present ideas and directions to the class as a whole. This often results in each child working alone even though he or she is alongside another child and even sharing materials. Initially, children seek confirmation of the correctness of an answer from the teacher, rather than from themselves, to support the logic of the solution. As the problems are refined and embedded into task activities that motivate a variety of strategies, teachers begin to recognize that they are less frequently leading and more often listening to children's explanations. Teachers' roles begin to shift from "telling and describing" to "listening and questioning" and "probing for understanding," although the shift occurs at varying rates and to varying extents among teachers. Skill and understanding in guiding and facilitating children's problem solving is a very individual accomplishment.

For children, there emerges increased freedom to invent procedures and to follow a variety of paths to solution. Some of these are unfamiliar to the teacher or are viewed as inefficient; however, as the teacher's role begins to shift to listening, asking questions with interest, and trying to follow the processes that the child is employing to build a solution, interest shifts to greater attention and value of children's thinking. For children, also, there is a steady increase in collaboration with classmates as the variety of possible solutions and curiosity about other models leads to a need for confirmation or clarification. For instance, two boys were working side by side to figure out and draw representations of particular fractions when one part was given. One of the boys was perplexed about representing a number greater than one and looked around for the teacher who did not immediately respond. The second boy considered the task and said: *"I see. One-half—This is one!"* He held up two blocks together to show his partner. Then he said: *"Then this is one and one-half."* His friend stared at the blocks and then exclaimed: *"Oh—I see!"* and with a smile immediately constructed a suitable representation for himself.

A third set of concerns expressed by many teachers relates to the development of better modes of assessment and record keeping of children's work in mathematics. Dissatisfied with their previous manner of grading, teachers are developing their own format to assist children in recording their problem-solving work. They are asking each child to draw a picture of the model built and to describe it symbolically. Some teachers are collecting students' solutions to each of the activities and building a portfolio for each child in order to note individual progress in children's ability to build representations. Analyses of children's work becomes the basis for revision of lesson activities as well as a mode of assessing individual children's progress. Teachers express that the ways in which concepts are built by students do not necessarily match the chronological order presented in the formal curriculum and that the mathematical ideas develop as a system that is built in pursuit of a meaningful understanding of a problem. One teacher indicated that her most important departure from this way of teaching was that she now had "insight into particular understandings and misconceptions of the children."

Becoming Philosophic About Teaching and Learning

With teachers' increased perception, however, comes growing dissatisfaction with mandated test instruments. Teachers indicate that they often are caught in a contradictory situation between institutional demands to strengthen the standardized test scores to which they are held accountable and the growing belief that the alternative approach is incompatible with the current view.

A successful partnership between project staff and teachers requires a trusting and working relationship. For project staff this means careful attention to the strain and tension that many teachers openly were sharing. The staff, although not directly concerned with accountibility to the traditional standard, needed to recognize institutional constraints without compromising their personal values about how children learn. At the same time, they wanted to work to help teachers achieve project goals, realizing that radical changes in both curriculum and assessment of children's knowledge would result.

At one project site, this was initially addressed by local changes in assessment. Teachers and administrators decided that there should be some problems on midyear and final examinations that allowed the children to model their solutions and explain mathematical concepts in terms of the physical representation that was built. Working together with colleagues, the curriculum supervisor, and project staff, such items were then added to the district tests and piloted as a part of the midyear evaluation. Teachers' evaluation of students' performance began to change in order to give more attention to the process of children's developing representations and problem solving, rather than to the accuracy with which procedures are applied to gain correct answers and acceptable scores on standardized achievement tests.

Some Results

The first district based project site was initiated in 1985 at the Harding School, a K-8 elementary school in Kenilworth, New Jersey. It began as a joint venture with the New Jersey Department of Higher Education, the Kenilworth Public Schools, and Rutgers University and involved the principal, curriculum coordinator, and all elementary school teachers responsible for teaching mathematics. Changes in both the perspective and the practice of the administrators and teachers indicate a growing professionalism and leadership in teaching mathematics. The principal and supervisor work with teachers as colleagues in curriculum decisions and carrying out classroom lessons. Teachers give presentations at professional conferences, serve as consultants and workshop leaders in other projects and in summer institutes. They regularly receive local and distant visitors who come to observe children doing mathematics. What is most dramatic in our observation is the teachers' movement from a direct instruction, telling model of teaching with emphasis on children's facility with symbols and computation to lessons in which children are actively constructing physical representations of mathematical ideas and procedures and then describing these models with appropriate symbols. The mathematics lessons usually begin with the posing of a problem which children are challenged to solve working together in pairs or small groups. Within the classroom environment a wide variety of manipulatable materials are made available to the children in order that they can construct physical representations of the problems to be solved. Children enjoy creating new problem situations for each other and data continue to show that mathematics is the favorite subject of the children.

The teacher's role within the classroom has changed to include a much greater concern for allowing children to build meaning into the mathematics they are studying. We observe teacher interaction with students that includes encouraging them to:

1. Find more than one way to approach and solve a problem,
2. Seek to understand the solutions of others, and
3. Accept responsibility for finding and correcting their own errors.

Another city-wide project, on a much larger scale, is currently in its second year with eleven schools in the urban district of New Brunswick, NJ. Preliminary analysis of teacher and student data indicates similar trends in growth for teachers and students.

The tension that is always present for teachers is evaluation of student performance based on standardized test score data. For Kenilworth, the mean achievement scores of the students, however, have risen from the low-middle range to the middle-high. Extensive analysis of children's performance over their five years in the project is currently in process. However, Dr. Jeffrey Smith, Director of Research and Development of the Graduate School of Education at Rutgers, provided us with a general review of Kenilworth standardized test score data from 1983 (when we started with some teacher workshops) to 1987 (when the more intensive level of participation of the Rutgers team was reduced). In his report, he wrote:

> In 1983, Kenilworth showed a test performance pattern very consistent with what one might expect from a program for the lower grades. There was a high performance across the board in grades 1-3 (mean percentile for reading = 88; math = 94.3). This dropped off some for grades 4-6 (reading = 76.3; math = 63.5). . . . The program started in the spring of 1983 with some workshops and became more intensive in the 1983-84 school year. Again, whether this is attributable to a *Hawthorne Effect* or more time allocated to math or some other reason cannot be determined. What is clear is that math performance improved substantially during that year at the junior high school level (7-8). The mean math score went from 63.5 to 85.5. At the same time, the reading scores for these same children dropped from 56.5 to 47.5, so the change cannot be attributable to a general increase in performance in the district. In 1985 there were some changes in the scores, but the pattern holds fairly constant. In 1987, the test form and norms changed. It is generally believed in the testing community that the new norms are more difficult than the old ones. The results for Kenilworth are as follows: (1) in reading, the scores were 1-3, 59.0; 4-6, 65.6; 7-8, 59.5; (2) in math, the scores were 1-3, 79.0; 4-6, 83.0; 7-8, 73.0. The math mean percentiles ranged from 13.5 to 20 percentile points higher than reading on the 1987 test for the grade ranges provided.
>
> The question becomes, *What does all of this mean?* I think the answer is fairly straightforward. Kenilworth has gone from being a district whose reading and math scores are in synch and fall over the years (a typical pattern) to one where the reading scores follow this pattern, but the math scores do not. The math scores look consistently stronger than reading and somewhat stronger than language. This pattern began in 1984 and continues to the present test. The drop overall in scores for 1987

> can probably be attributed to new norms and the fact that the district hasn't *adjusted* to the new test. This is common when a district adopts a new test. The strength of the 1987 results is in the relative performance in math compared to reading. (excerpt from the Annual Report of the Rutgers-Kenilworth Teacher Development in Mathematics Project to the New Jersey State Department of Higher Education, 1988)

Smith's analysis of these scores suggests to us that a rise in standardized test scores in mathematics as compared with reading might be explained by the changes occurring in classroom instruction. Teachers are paying more attention to how children think; they are moving away from giving students procedures to find solutions the teacher's way and are becoming more attentive to the way their *students* think about problems.

Chapter 11: On The Knowledge of Mathematics Teachers

Leslie P. Steffe
University of Georgia

There are two fundamental constraints on improving mathematics education at the precollege level. The first is that mathematics teachers, due at least in part to the enormous amount of energy and time that they expend teaching, seldom engage in mathematical explorations in a search for insights and unifying concepts in the mathematics that they could possibly teach (Steffe, Shrum, Clifton, Hart, & Ireland, 1985). While many study collegiate mathematics in a quest for an advanced degree or certification, the work involved in translating some form of that mathematics into their teaching is prohibitive. They take what appears in school mathematics textbooks as a given and the gap between collegiate mathematics and the mathematics that they teach is seldom bridged.

Practically, mathematics teachers are not able to develop an encompassing network of mathematical concepts that could deepen, unify, and extend *their* conceptions of school mathematics. Such a network, however could provide them with a rich resource from which they could draw. It could be used as a foundation for operationally defining fundamental mathematical concepts, including rational numbers, real numbers, variables, and a host of others. It could be used also in generating and posing problems from which mathematical concepts are to be learned. Finally, it could provide the teacher with unifying concepts and methods that they could use to rise above the current compartmentalization found in school mathematics textbooks. This is particularly critical because the adaptations of teachers are in the direction of the textbook presentations rather than in the direction of an encompassing network of mathematical relations.

The second key element is that mathematics teachers find it very difficult to change their teaching strategies. Researchers in the Second International Study of Mathematics found that current mathematics teaching almost universally can be characterized as formal, symbolic presentations of mathematical rules or procedures in lecture formats (McKnight, 1987). Teachers who are mathematically inactive usually present mathematics as static, dualistic (either right or wrong), and as consisting of routine procedures. Solving "simultaneous" linear equations, for example, might be demonstrated as a sequence of steps that, if followed, would yield a correct answer. While such procedural knowledge is basic, too often teaching starts and ends with the procedures and mathematics learning is not based on experience, intuition, or insight.

Byers (1983) has cogently argued that many of the problems associated with mathematics teaching and learning follow from a formalist/structuralist conception of mathematics that downgrades the value of human experience and intuition.

> What the student is exposed to is a formal, sanitized version of the subject. Over the years every hint of struggle and controversy has been wiped clean ... the mathematical world that is presented to the student is . . . completely intimidating. Yet this very student goes on to be a mathematics teacher (Byers, 1983, p. 23).

These comments were meant for college mathematics education, but according to McKnight (1987), they are relevant to precollege mathematics education as well. This version of mathematics *encourages* rote mathematics teaching because if, as Byers (1983) says, "there is a feeling that some ultimate mathematical reality is embedded in these abstract structures" (p. 32), then the teachers' search for mathematical meaning can begin and end with the formal, symbolic presentations of rules and procedures. Such teachers might be shocked to learn, say, that the rules for multiplication of signed numbers that they have taught as unassailable truths could be changed and an internally consistent number system developed.

There is clearly a need for mathematics teachers to experience a change in world view. Adopting the belief that mathematics is a human activity and that mathematical meaning is constructed as a result of such activity would be a step towards alleviating the influence of formalism and the abstracted, symbolic presentations of mathematical rules and procedures that it encourages. The belief can have far reaching consequences for mathematics teaching.

Attempts to influence the world view of mathematics teachers are most appropriately made in the context of their ongoing mathematical activity. Rather than select novel subject matter, however, I place the teachers in possible mathematical environments that are seemingly familiar to them. In doing so, it is one of my intentions that the teachers deepen their meaning of the mathematical concepts that they teach.

Mathematical Meaning

The most fundamental job facing mathematics teachers is to foster the development of mathematical meaning in their students. René Thom (1973), in a paper given at the Second International Congress on Mathematical Education, takes the existence of mathematical objects as synonymous with meaning.

> The real problem which confronts mathematics teaching is not that of rigor, but the problem of the development of 'meaning', of the 'existence' of mathematical objects (p. 202).

"Existence" is taken as existence in the *mental world*—"It is to this primordial task of conferring on it *existence* in the mental world, that teaching must be dedicated" (Thom, 1973,

p. 202). A mathematical object "exists" or has meaning when it enters into the realm of consciousness. Thom believes that the role of the teacher is that of a midwife—"to bring a foetus to maturity and, when the moment comes, to free it from the mother-structure which engenders it" (p. 201). How these "mother structures" might be understood has been the subject of considerable debate (Piattelli-Palmarini, 1980). The Piagetian position that they are not mental entities that are programmed to unfold over time provides the teacher with a central and most critical role in their formation.

> These structures exist in what the children I study "do" ..But even if I am in favor of an endogenous origin of structures, this does not at all mean that they are innate in their successive states for me a divergence seems to remain in regard to the necessity of substituting for innateness a mechanism of continual construction (Piaget, 1980b, p. 283).

In other words, Piaget "saw" operative structure *in the actions of children* and thus traced the origins of mathematical knowledge to such goal-directed activity. These organized, purposeful action patterns were called "scheme" by Piaget. "All action that is repeatable or generalized through application to new objects engenders by this very fact a 'scheme'" (Piaget, 1980c, p. 24).

Mathematical Knowledge as Scheme

In the constructivist school, there is a conviction that conceptual knowledge cannot be transferred ready-made from one person to another, but must be built up by every knower solely on the basis of his or her own experience.

> I think that human knowledge is essentially active. To know is to assimilate reality into systems of transformations .I find myself opposed to the view of knowledge as a copy, a passive copy, of reality (Piaget, 1970a, p. 15).

Schemes are the primary instruments of assimilation and are compatible with what Bridgman (1934) called operational definition.

> The meaning that I ascribe to "beautiful," for example, I find in the operations which I perform, or more simply, in what I do (p. 104).

The primary difference between Bridgman's operational definitions and Piaget's schemes is that the former refer to the mathematician's (or physicist's) knowledge and the latter to the child's knowledge. But they are not different in kind because both refer to the conceptual activity of the knower.

Whether meaning is to be found in the operations an individual performs or in results of performing the operations is related to "where the knower is." That is, if the knower is aware of the structure of his or her actions—if the knower is "above" the activity "looking down" on it—then meaning could be found in the activity as well as in its result. On the other hand, if the structure of the actions is not within the awareness of the knower, it would be very difficult indeed for the knower to find meaning in the activity. In the case of "beautiful," for example, I am not aware whatsoever of the operations that I use, so they are certainly not meaningful to me. Nevertheless, what I take as being beautiful is known to me as I can consider those results of operating as what I mean by the term. Given this philosophy of meaning, what can be done to foster mathematical meanings in the mathematics teacher? There are essentially two possible answers to that question—encourage their mathematical activity and encourage their *reflection on that activity* (Kilpatrick, 1986; Steffe & Cobb, 1983).

From here I will proceed by choosing the example of the problem of fostering meaning of the square root of two and sketching an outline of the steps that seem to me to be necessary to develop an operational definition *in the case of the mathematics teacher*. For the sake of brevity, I will assume that the teachers know what it means to find the area of a rectangle whose sides each are of length some rational number as well as what it means for any rational number to be expressed as a terminating decimal or a nonterminating repeating decimal, which requires knowledge of the geometric series (Wertheimer, 1959, Appendix 6). Of course, these assumptions are made only for the purpose of writing the paper.

The Square Root of Two

Given a unit square, it is possible to proceed on two different bases. The problem can be posed of finding a square of area two or of finding the length of a diagonal of a unit square. I choose the former. This can be done as in Figure 1. Taking the area of the inscribed square as one, it requires insight to produce a circumscribed square of area two. The question of the length of its sides becomes a natural one to ask.

Whatever these lengths are, each is denoted by c. Using the results of finding area in the case of squares whose sides are rational lengths, we see that if c stands for the length of a side, then $c \times c = 2$. Whatever the unknown c is, it stands for the length of a side of the square of area two. However, we cannot yet know with any certainty what c might be. Our first approach is to attempt to find a rational number for c. That is, can we find a terminating or repeating decimal which, if squared, would yield two?

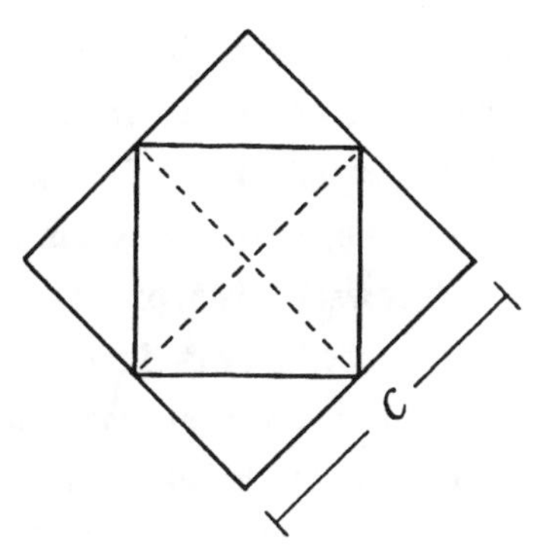

Figure 1 - A Square of Area Two

At this point, it is very appropriate for the teachers to write a computer program that will produce such a decimal. Writing such a program also requires insight for it involves finding a procedure that will yield a decimal whose square is within a specified distance of two as well as a program to produce a sequence of such decimals. A program to produce a sequence of such decimals constitutes an operational definition of *c* (see Bridgman, 1934, p. 227 for a justification). The essence of such a program is that it will produce a sequence of terminating decimals that differ from *c* by no more than some specified amount. At this point, we may say that one meaning of *c* is to be found in the structure of the operations that the programmer used to write the program.

The result of running the program (which is also a meaning of *c*) is a sequence of decimals whose squares are approximations of the area of the square of side *c*. This sequence of decimals should feed back into the original problem, yielding a nested sequence of expanding squares that is bounded by the original square. The concept of the area of a square should now include the approximating procedure.

Another meaning of *c* is that it is the length of the side of a square of area two and $(2)^{1/2}$ is a symbol for that length. One last question remains: *Is $(2)^{1/2}$ a nonterminating but repeating decimal?* This question cannot be answered by inspection of any particular decimal of the sequence or the sequence itself and relies on logical argument. That is, the operational definition does not fully characterize the square root of two even though we can conjecture that it is not a repeating decimal. There must be mechanisms of reasoning outside of the operational definition—there must be logical reasoning.

Learning Mathematical Concepts

Mathematics instruction has not yet benefited from the constructivist principle that each individual must construct his or her own representations of reality. Scant attention is given to mathematics as a human activity and the mathematical activity of the individual is essentially ignored. The vestiges of meaning theory that remain in current approaches to mathematics teaching hark back to two historically important schools of thought. One principal contributor to *the structural school* believed that "meaning is to be sought in the structure, the organization, the relationships of the subject itself" (Brownell, 1945, p. 481). The origin of a second school, *the operational school* can be traced to Percy Bridgman's operational analysis of fundamental concepts. Van Engen (1949), the principal contributor to this school, believed that the meaning of a symbol is "an intention to act and . . . the act need not, in itself, take place. However, if the individual is challenged to demonstrate the meaning of the symbol, then the action takes place" (p. 324). Van Engen viewed semantics as operational definitions. These operational definitions were taken to be universal and, therefore, identical for all students. Especially in mathematics, the main concepts seemed transparent and were expected to become "self-evident," provided they were properly explained.

Constructivism has made me aware of the highly complex processes of abstraction that underlie mathematical understanding. If we believe, as did Van Engen and Bridgman, that the meaning of a mathematical symbol is essentially an action, then it follows that mathematical concepts will be learned by means of abstraction based upon actions as well as sensory impressions. Indeed, Piaget (1970a) characterized "reflective abstraction" as:

> the mode of abstraction that derives its knowledge from actions and from the subject's operations. Thus defined, reflective abstraction is necessarily constructive and enlarges and enriches the structures from which it starts (p. 221).

The realization that schemes can function on different levels of abstraction makes it plausible to think of mathematical concepts in that context. It also provides a possible psychological interpretation for the astute statement made by Thom quoted earlier. I interpret the "existence" of mathematical objects as psychological existence—existence as concepts in the context of schemes.

A scheme includes the individual's *conception of situations* in which a particular activity takes place. In other words, the individual structures experiential situations in terms of his or her concepts. In Piaget's (1964) words, "the response is there first, or . . . at the beginning there is structure" (p. 15). These structures may constitute concepts. The term "concept" is taken as referring to "any structure that has been abstracted from the process of experiential abstraction as recurrently usable" (von Glasersfeld, 1982, p. 194). A concept can, on the one hand, be used in assimilatory activity and thereby guide further activity and, on the other hand, it can be informed by the activity that it guides. It is an anticipatory structure which guides activity within a goal directed framework, where anticipation is "nothing other than

. . . application of the schema (or scheme) . . . to a new situation before it actually happens" (Piaget, 1971a, p. 195).

The view of a mathematical concept as a scheme abstracted from activity—as a program comprising procedures—raises the question of how such a concept might be learned. Minimally, learning involves a process of experiential abstraction (i.e., abstraction in or as a result of an experience). Whatever experiential situation is structured by the individual, the activity of structuring involves an assimilation of the situation using currently available concepts:

> The fundamental relation involved in all learning is not association. I think that the fundamental relation is one of assimilation the integration of any sort of reality into a structure which seems to me to be the fundamental relation from the point of view of pedagogical or didactic applications (Piaget, 1964, p. 18).

The emphasis is placed on the activity of the individual and reflection on that activity. Piaget believed that without activity, there would be no possible pedagogy that would significantly transform the learner.

Assimilation, however, does not account for learning. Mathematics learning consists in the *adaptations* that individuals make in their functioning schemes as a result of their experiences. These adaptations can occur prior to activity, in the context of the activity, as a result of periods of mathematical activity, or during periods of rest or reflection (Cobb & Steffe, 1983; Hadamard, 1945).

Learning and Problem Solving

Learning as defined is compatible with what Polya (1962) meant when he stated that to have a problem means "to search consciously for some action appropriate to attain a clearly conceived, but not immediately attainable, aim" (p. 117). For those individuals who can find an appropriate action sequence to achieve their aim, their assimilatory concepts will be necessarily modified and the problem-solving activity can be intrinsically satisfying. Papert (1980) has suggested that, "Anything is easy if you can assimilate it to your collection of models. If you can't, anything can be painfully difficult. . . . What an individual can learn, and how he learns it, depends on what models he has available" (p. vii).

Even when assimilation is possible, mathematical problem solving can be painfully difficult. What makes it so can be a result of a lack of insight. While insight may seem to be mystical, without it, problems of any substance would not be solved. In discussing insight or "seeing the light" Wertheimer (1959) commented:

> What a change, when all the parts suddenly form a consistent clear whole, in a new orientation, in strong reorganization and recentering, all fitting the structural requirements (p. 57).

While it is not possible to do a complete analysis of insight, it can be profitably thought of as a *coordination* of previously learned concepts. Insight and adaptation are compatible since adaptation involves elaborations and reorganizations of currently available schemes. Essentially, adaptation *encompasses* insight and learning encompasses problem solving. In mathematics, problem solving is a *crucial* aspect of learning mathematical concepts. A primary goal of problem solving is to encourage individuals to elaborate and reorganize their concepts.

Arithmetic Series

We have already seen how a concept of area can be modified through solving problems. Arithmetic series are used as another example. The differences in this example and in the example of the square root of two reside in the *variety of solution procedures that are encouraged.* This is not to say, however, that alternative operational definitions should be discouraged in the case of the square root of two, for that would be a repudiation of one of the basic tenets of constructivism. That discussion dealt with explicating the nature of an operational definition in one of the most difficult areas of school mathematics, whereas the current discussion is devoted to how a teacher *might* construct such an operational definition—a concept.

Even though most mathematics teachers know that the sum of the first n integers can be found by multiplying the last integer of the series by its successor and then dividing that product by two, mathematics teachers might not understand that there is a *solution process* that can be transposed to find the sum of the first n *even* or *odd* integers (Wertheimer, 1959). The teachers know what the sum of the first n integers means, but their concept usually comprises only iterative procedures. If that is the case, when teaching the formula, a mathematics teacher would unavoidably teach their students in the same blind, procedural way that they understand it. A teacher might demonstrate a process for finding the sum as follows:

$$\begin{array}{rcl} S & = & 1 + 2 + 3 + \ldots + n \\ \underline{S} & \underline{=} & \underline{n + (n-1) + (n-2) + \ldots + 1} \\ 2S & = & (n+1) + (n+1) + (n+1) + \ldots + (n+1) \end{array}$$

$$\text{Therefore, } S = n(n+1)/2$$

Even if this solution process is an insightful one for the teacher, it is usually not *produced* by his or her students. Such a teacher or textbook demonstration can intimidate even the strongest mathematics students and lead them to accept the formula without insight and on the authority of the teacher or textbook. It is something to be memorized rather than something to be created. The possibility that mathematics students could produce such an insightful solution is usually overlooked for whatever reason and the students' mathematical activity is not encouraged. As a consequence, if the students encounter the problem of finding the sum of the first n even (or odd) integers, they usually view it as a problem not related to the previously solved problem even though it contains analogous procedures. There is no attempt to make a transposition of a solution process for the simple reason that there is not a solution process available to them.

If *mathematics teachers* produce the formula insightfully, restructuring a graphical interpretation, then it becomes possible for them to transpose the method to the problem of finding the sum of the first n even (or odd) integers (Wertheimer, 1959, pp. 108ff). In Figure 2, an insightful solution of the problem of finding the sum of the first six integers is presented.

One insightful solution is usually not sufficient for teachers to make the transpositions to arithmetic series in general. Other examples are essential. Moreover, no attempts should be made to control how the teachers restructure the graphical presentation of the series. The only

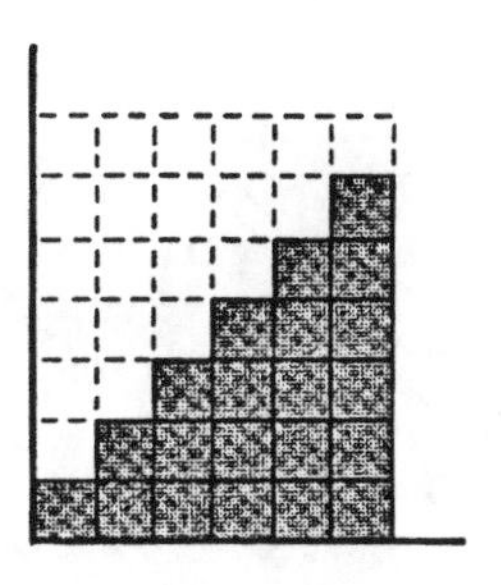

Figure 2 - Finding the sum of the first six integers
by doubling the sum.

suggestion that might be made is to draw the graph. Consequently, various methods of restructuring should be forthcoming, like in Figure 3.

At this point the teachers might be asked to interpret their restructured graphs and to resolve the differences in the two (or more) interpretations.

Another important context for finding the sum of the series is presented in Figure 4. Again, the teachers would be asked to find how this relates to the preceding two.

There is also the method exemplified in Figure 5. The first three columns are built by adding the last three columns to the first three; the last to the first, etc. Since we have (6 + 1) blocks in each row and 6/2 rows, there are (6 + 1) x 6/2 blocks. Were the number of original columns odd, we first could find an average number of blocks per column and then take that times the number columns.

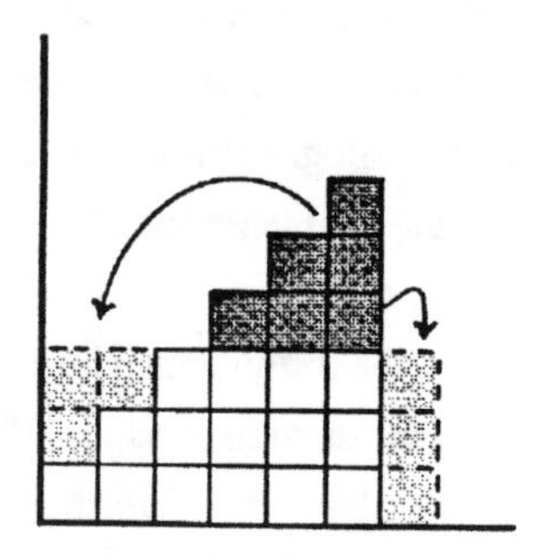

Figure 3 - Finding the sum of the first six integers by equalizing summands.

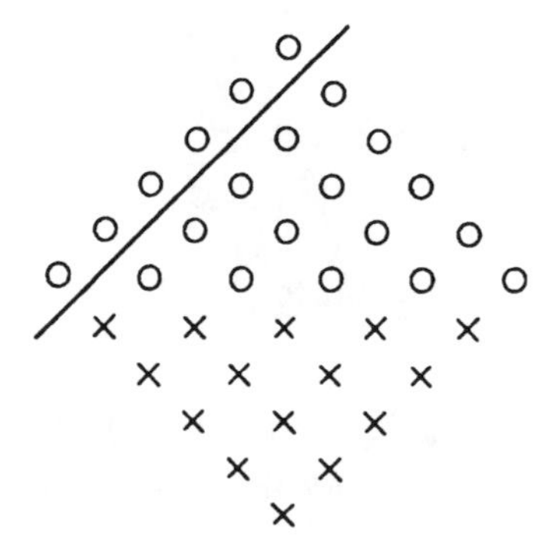

Figure 4 - Finding the sum of the first six integers by completing a " Pascal " square

It should be easy to observe that each of these methods is quite distinct from the demonstration using symbols in spirit as well as in *who has the insight.* Eventually, the general case (find the sum of the first n integers) should be presented and the teachers allowed to generalize whatever method seems most natural to them to generate the sum of the series. Finding the sum of the first n even (or odd) integers is now a distinct possibility by transposing the abstracted method of finding the sum of the first n integers. The solutions of the teachers to the above tasks serve as a basis for continuing the work of developing the concept of arithmetic series.

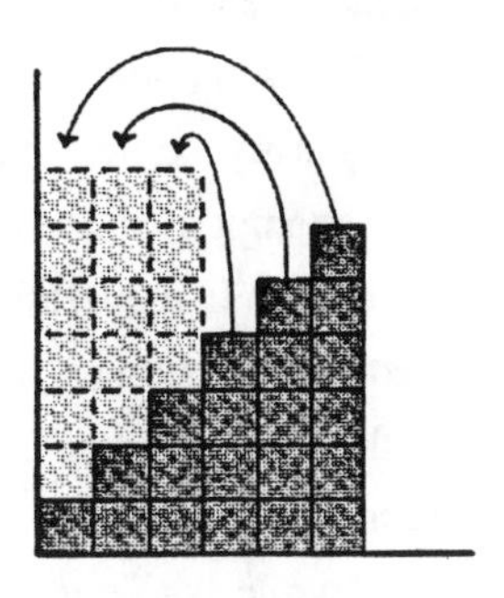

Figure 5 - Finding the sum of the first six integers
by adding ordered pairs by summands

My observation is that if teachers experience the productive thought that leads to insightful solutions and reflect on their thought processes, they can then see creative possibilities for their students. The teachers, being sensitive to their own recent mathematical experiences, see links between their experience and the possible experience of their students. In fact, if mathematics teachers are asked to decenter and to reflect on their experiences of doing mathematics and to project what those experiences mean for how they teach mathematics in their classrooms, they are able to verbalize teaching strategies to foster the mathematical learning of their students.

Socialization in Solving Problems

The change in world view that has been suggested shifts the focus of "teaching" from the activity of the teacher to the activity of the students *as understood by the teacher*. In the teaching episodes that have as a goal the construction of unifying—assimilating—concepts by the teachers, I make a concerted attempt to organize my activities in such a way that the mathematical activities of the participating teachers is maximized. As an example of a unifying concept, I pose problems of finding the path of a point that moves under certain constraints. Specifically, the teachers are asked to find the path of the point that moves in such a way that it always remains equidistant from a given point and a given line.

Assimilating the Problem

The initial focus is on the participating teachers' assimilation of the problem. I concur with Polya that this essential aspect of solving a problem cannot be overlooked. I encourage the teachers to discuss, among themselves, the essential elements of the problem. Phrases such as "points equidistant from a given line" or "a given point" may not be understood or understood with distortion (from my point of view). It is my explicit intention to encourage mathematical conversations among the teachers as they attempt to understand the problem. By encouraging them to intensively discuss a particular problem in preparation for solving it, a context is created where I illustrate my premise that understanding a problem can be a dialectical process involving the assimilation of the essential problem elements into current mental models of the problem and testing the results of that assimilation through dialogue with one's peers—which encourages the process of assimilation. My role as a "midwife" is fulfilled in this microcosmic case because the teachers are able to reflect on their visualized re-presentations of the moving point.

The Search Activity

Once the participating teachers feel that they understand the problem in much the same way as the other teachers and that everyone has an agreed upon aim, they may turn to the search activity as described by Polya—to the construction of a new scheme. It is here that I play my most essential role as a teacher. An agreed upon goal can be enough to initiate search activity and to sustain it for a period of time. However, in a problem that is as difficult as the construction problem that I have posed, the search activity may not lead to a solution. As teacher, I must make decisions whether to encourage independent search activity or to socialize the search activity (Lochhead, 1983b). In either case, the search activities of the teachers must be supported.

Ultimately, the solution of the problem involves the coordination of two or more concepts—say, the paths of points equidistant from a given line (a family of parallel lines) and the paths of points equidistant from a given point (a family of concentric circles). In those cases where I perceive the teachers reaching frustration in their search activities, I do make suggestions to renew or guide their searches. But there is never any guarantee that a teacher engages in the productive thinking that would yield the coordination. However, he or she might be at a place in his or her search process that a discussion of the solution could be productive. In any event, I am faced with the decision of when to ask a solver (or solvers) who claim to have a solution to demonstrate it.

My purpose for asking for a demonstration is three fold. First, I ask the participating teachers to inspect the alleged solution to check its validity. This encourages critical thinking—

the ability to follow and evaluate a logical argument. Second, I ask for any solutions that appear to be an alternative. This encourages the attitude that there may be more than one solution and adds to the mathematical flexibility of the teachers. *It also sensitizes them to the reasoning of others and encourages decentering from their own thought processes in an attempt to understand the thinking of others.* This is an essential attitude for a mathematics teacher if he or she is to encourage the mathematical activity of his or her students. Third, the unsuccessful teachers can engage in the discussion of the alleged solutions and thereby finally produce their own actions that yield their personal solution. Hopefully, they feel that they could have produced the actions had they only looked at the problem differently or had thought to do the particular thing that was essential. In any event, they are in a state whereby they can learn someone else's solution, which is quite preferable to my demonstrating it before they have any chance of attempting to solve the problem. I do not denigrate the power of a lucid "explanation" by a knowing person nor do I discourage the teachers from making such explanations. However, I do encourage that those explanations be offered at the most favorable moments—after they have been involved in the intellectual activity that is required to make sense of them.

Feedback

The socialization of the problem solution through the discussions that I have suggested plays an essential role in the problem-solving process. It provides a context for looking back on the shared solutions and abstracting their salient elements. Reflection on the solutions is essential for consolidating and refining them. My goal is for the solutions to feed back into the original assimilating concept, reorganizing and extending that concept. This is an essential step in learning mathematics.

The lack of meaningful mathematical conversations is all too characteristic in mathematics classrooms. For whatever reason, students are encouraged to work independently in mathematics without fulfilling the basic need of every human being to communicate with their peers. I believe that it is essential that the students' construction of mathematical reality be a part of their social construction of reality. *As mathematics teachers, we must strive to make mathematical conversations as commonplace as, say, political conversations. Certainly, mathematical conversations must start but hopefully not end, in the mathematics classrooms.*

Periods in the Learning Process

Periods in the solution of a particular problem have been identified: assimilating the problem, the search process which might lead to a solution, and feedback—an integration of the solutions and the assimilating concepts. There are also more global periods in the learning of mathematical concepts.

The Constructive Period

In the case of the problem of constructing the path of a point that moves in such a way that it always remains equidistant from a given line and a given point, if a construction method is found, the method itself does not completely specify the path even though the solver might be able to sketch a trace of the path—it does not provide an analytical expression of the path. A new problem must be posed that contributes to, but that is not solved by, the solution of the original problem.

This new problem involves embedding the moving point in a coordinate system and posing the problem of finding the relation between the x-coordinate and the y-coordinate of the moving point P expressed in coordinate form. This general problem can be posed in many particular instances. For example, the given point could be taken on the x-axis, say (5,0), and the given line may be taken as the y-axis. Decisions have to be made concerning what problems are posed and to whom. In other words, the teachers must be good *problem posers* (Brown & Walter, 1983). When posing a problem, there must be an analysis of whether the particular individual for whom the problem is intended has a chance to solve it. Are the relevant concepts that are needed for solution available? What subproblems need to be solved before a problem involving those concepts is posed? Should the student be thrown into an "open search" experience where the problem is quite far removed from their current concepts? All of these are decisions that the teacher must make and there is no available decision matrix known to me except my knowledge of mathematics and of the students' concepts and problem solving ability. Simply put, I rely on my best judgment for particular students in a particular context. In fact, the students should be involved in selecting the problems on which they want to work. It is my job as the teacher to have a rich array of possible problems available.

The Period of Retroactive Thematization

Work on these initial problems constitutes a very important period in the overall learning of the mathematical concepts that I, as teacher, have in mind for the students' to learn. However, my observation is that while the period of discussion and reflection for particular problems is critical, it is necessary to review the solutions of several problems and reorganize their elements in retroactive thematization (Piaget, 1980c) in order to realize a concept in a general and symbolic form. For example, the problem of characterizing the graph of any quadratic equation represents such a retroactive thematization if it can be solved. It should follow the constructive work that has been suggested because it requires that the products of that work be viewed in light of a new but critical question. While the teachers might know that a point that moves under the stated constraints yields an equation of the second degree, there is no guarantee that any quadratic equation has a graph that is a parabola. Asking this new question opens up a host of new interpretations of the old concepts. It provides a "top down" perspective on the products of "bottom up" processing (Cooper & Clancy, 1982). During this period of retroactive thematization, written text, where the past work is organized and discussed, can provide a source to which the students can turn for consolidation and reflection.

The Period of Assimilating Generalization

What makes learning interesting is the possibility of generalization of a concept. If the concept is a dynamic structure in the mental life of the individual rather than an isolated piece of knowledge, then new problem situations that the concept illuminates should offer exciting possibilities for assimilating generalization. While one could view this period as a period of application of the concept, that distorts its meaning somewhat. In my experience, the concept is *reconstructed* in the new situations, not simply applied. This process of continual reconstruction broadens and deepens the concept. It essentially changes the concept to include some of the problems that it can solve and the new operations necessary for their solution.

A Network of Mathematical Concepts

It is not possible to elaborate an encompassing network of mathematical concepts for the mathematics teacher in a short paper such as this. An indication can be given, however, of the flavor of such a network. The idea of a moving point is one of the unifying concepts that is currently ignored in school mathematics. It can be used in the development of the equations of a line in the plane as well as in the development of the equations of the line in space, the parabola, the circle, the ellipse, and the hyperbola. More generally, it can serve as a geometrical basis for the development of variable and function.

The Pythagorean theorem is another unifying concept that is not used enough in secondary school mathematics. Learning the concept should proceed by problem solving and insight. Interestingly enough, von Glasersfeld (1981) has suggested that the geometrical configuration of Figure 1 led Pythagoras to invent the relation that goes by his name. Looking at that configuration in two ways (Figure 6) suggests a special case of the relation. Bruni (1977) has provided a more general solution (Figure 7). Neither of these solutions is widely known by mathematics teachers.

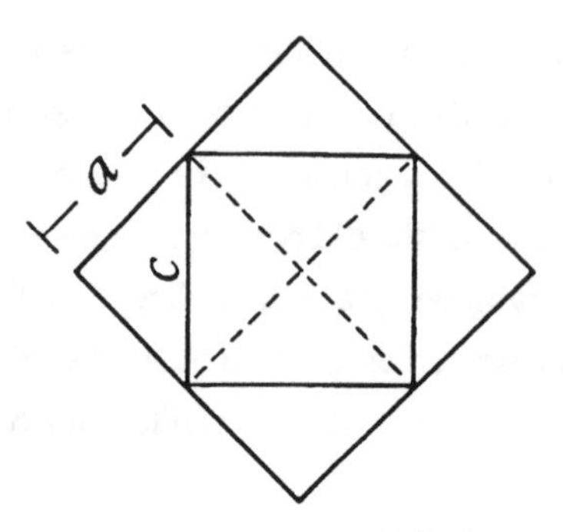

Area of larger square = $4\ a^2$
Area of larger square = $c^2 + 4\ (\ a^2\ /\ 2\ )$
Therefore, $c^2 = 2\ a^2$

Figure 6 - Initial Pythagorean Relation

They are within the reach of beginning algebra students because of their elegant geometrical simplicity. They do involve a great deal of insight to produce, however, and offer interesting research possibilities for mathematics educators.

The relations are based in partitioning a square in two different ways. Producing the partitions is where deep insight is required and should be carefully studied. Moreover, operativity of the concept is always at issue even for those students who do produce the solution through insight. But that can be said for any other concept as well.

The Pythagorean theorem can serve as a basis for the development of the real and complex numbers. While this is usually not emphasized in school mathematics, the lack of centrality of the generalization of the Pythagorean theorem—the law of cosines—is even more puzzling. In trigonometry, for example, the Pythagorean identities are developed as implications of the Pythagorean theorem—the most basic being $\sin^2 a + \cos^2 a = 1$. But the so-called non-Pythagorean identities are developed using what I consider to be nonintuitive methods. Seldom is it appreciated that the angle sum and difference formulas are but implications of the law of cosines, which is itself an implication of the Pythagorean theorem. Using the law of cosines, the most basic "non-Pythagorean" identity is $\cos(a - b) = \cos a \cos b + \sin a \sin b$, from which the others follow.

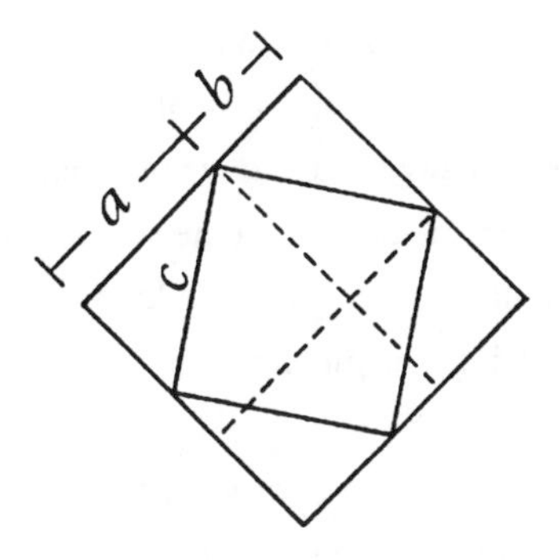

Area of larger square = $a^2 + b^2 + 2ab$
Area of larger square = $c^2 + 4(ab/2)$
Therefore, $c^2 = a^2 + b^2$

Figure 7 - General Pythagorean Relation

Trigonometry is one content area that could be profitably reorganized using the law of cosines. Another is the work with vectors. The inner product of two vectors is a concept that is based directly on the law of cosines interpreted in a coordinate system. It is an operation that has deep roots in the Pythagorean theorem but, yet, one that is capriciously defined for the students with no reference to the law of cosines. The inner product of two vectors is easy to compute but difficult to understand. Further, few students realize that it is a generalization of multiplication of real numbers.

A third area that could be made accessible to precollege mathematics students, if their teachers knew the law of cosines and how it relates to geometry, is the equation of a plane in space. Students are inevitably puzzled by why the equation of a line in space looks different than the equation of a line in the plane, while the equation of a plane in space is the analogue of the equation of the line in the plane. The law of cosines can be a unifying concept for these two analogous equations and can eliminate the necessity of prematurely using vector methods as a basis for their development.

My argument is that the Pythagorean theorem and its generalization provides a deep unifying—assimilating—concept for what otherwise can be disparate topics. It is ironical that, for example, the inner product of two vectors is used to develop the equation of the plane in space without that operation being solidly grounded in the law of cosines. In fact, the inner product of two vectors is but an *abstraction* based on the law of cosines. So, we could only expect great discontinuities in mathematical understanding to be the result of defining the inner product of two vectors without reference to its "mother structure" and then using that definition to develop a concept as important as the equation of a plane in space of a line in the plane.

Mathematics teachers desperately need to develop a network of insights and unifying concepts in the mathematics that they could possibly teach. Currently, they find themselves in the position of teaching what is in the textbook without knowing that there are alternatives that are possibly more viable in promoting student learning.

Final Comments

My thesis has been that a change in the world view of mathematics teachers is necessary if there are to be major reforms in precollege mathematical education. Teachers' current beliefs that school mathematics is a static and unchanging "discipline" comprising algebra I, geometry, algebra II, and advanced algebra is steeped in traditional values as well as in their view of the nature of mathematics (Cooney, 1985). Focusing on mathematics as a human activity does not change the fact that teachers have to make decisions about what mathematics to teach. But it does change their view of themselves as mathematical "beings," because they can no longer point to a textbook as the primary source of the mathematical knowledge that they teach. They must look inward and become aware of their own mathematical knowledge and use that knowledge to reorganize what they teach.

Viewing school mathematics as not being *a priori* can be exciting as well as challenging. It can give teachers a sense of control that is based squarely on their view of the nature of knowledge. Sharing in the responsibility of choosing the mathematics that they teach can lead teachers to once again become mathematically active—an activity that can be facilitated in educational environments where they seriously re-construct the mathematical knowledge that they once thought only they understood.

Improving mathematical education in the schools starts with improvements in the mathematical knowledge of teachers. If teachers could only accept the premise that the mathematical knowledge of their students is also valid, then the necessary adaptations of teachers when teaching mathematics would be in the direction of the *mathematical knowledge of their students* as well as in the direction of their own mathematical knowledge. In other words, the mathematical knowledge of the students as seen by their teachers would become part of the knowledge of the teachers. This happy state of affairs could only improve mathematical communication in the classroom, especially in those cases where the teachers emphasize the activity of their students in learning mathematics.

CONCLUSIONS

Chapter 12: Suggestions for the Improvement of Mathematics Education

Robert B. Davis, Rutgers University
Carolyn A. Maher, Rutgers University
Nel Noddings, Stanford University

The preceding chapters make several things clear. The idea of "constructivism"—hardly mentioned a few years ago—nowadays attracts a lot of attention in the world of mathematics education. A great many people now think and write about it, and the people who do so do not entirely agree with one another. Some who sympathize with the general pedagogical program suggested by constructivists find difficulties in the theoretical exposition of constructivism. These people ask: Is constructivism an epistemology, or is it a post-epistemological position? If the former, what are its views on truth, necessity, and evidence? If the latter, where are its discussions of the political nature of knowledge, competing communities, and power? These are all serious matters for constructivist theoreticians to consider.

Still, beneath the theoretical argumentation, there is a substantial agreement about the nature of learners, the nature of mathematics, and appropriate forms of pedagogy. Constructivists have even begun to address the issue raised by Noddings in chapter 1: namely, how can we differentiate knowledge from nonknowledge on the basis of construction if we believe that all mental acts are constructive? Confrey suggests in response that we might do well to speak of "weak" and "strong" acts of construction. Rote learning, then, would fall into the set of weak constructions. Clearly, there is much work, both conceptual and empirical, to be done in describing weak and strong constructions and the circumstances under which they are manifested.

Constructivists agree that mathematical learning involves the active manipulation of meanings, not just numbers and formulas. They reject the notion that mathematics is learned in a cumulative, linear fashion. Every stage of learning involves a search for meaning, and the acquisition of rote skills in no way ensures that learners will be able to use these skills intelligently in mathematical settings. Misconceptions may develop anywhere in the process, and constructivist teachers are continually watching for them and planning activities that will lead students to challenge their own faulty conceptions.

Constructivists recommend providing learning environments in which students can acquire basic concepts, algorithmic skills, heuristic processes, and habits of cooperation and reflection. These are all capabilities that should be generally useful in the future as well as the present and may well be vital in dealing with problem situations and solution strategies that no one at present can foresee. In such environments, the ideas which the student is learning become our main concern. Although these ideas are best learned by relating concepts unmistakably to some of the relevant procedures (see, e.g., Hiebert, 1986), the concepts themselves are imperfectly revealed by the more obvious kinds of "performance" data—one often gets correct answers by using methods that are built on flagrantly imperfect conceptual foundations, as a large research literature makes clear (see, e.g., Davis & McKnight, 1980; Erlwanger, 1973). We then have no real choice but to deal carefully with misconceptions, and we are required to concern ourselves with those experiences that are likely to give rise to some of the more pernicious misconceptions, and, conversely, with those experiences that protect against them. There is still a vast amount of research required in this area: What misconceptions arise regularly in given topics and processes? What kind of learner is most subject to a particular misconception? What activities successfully challenge particular misconceptions? What diagnostic techniques are especially effective in probing for various misconceptions?

Constructivism does not offer pedagogical recipes or convenience. It asks much of us. Many familiar tools, and many familiar attitudes, must be questioned, modified, or just plain discarded. We can no longer rely on the fact that a student has demonstrated a "performance"—has added fractions correctly, or solved a quadratic equation—to assure us that everything is just as it needs to be. Correct performance or not, the student may have some seriously wrong ways of thinking about mathematics, and these errors will prove powerful, and harmful, in the long run, even if they do not on today's test.

Nor is that the only way in which constructivism inconveniences us. If indeed a student does misunderstand, constructivism tells us that merely showing the student "the right way to do the problem" will probably not suffice to straighten things out. We must probe deeper, and make contact with the student's ways of thinking. This is where a repertoire of sophisticated diagnostic tools is essential.

What mathematics should students learn? The traditional approach assumed that learning facts and algorithms would lead more or less naturally to successful application in appropriate situations. We are now quite sure that this is untrue. Constructivism says that we must help students develop more powerful ways of thinking. We must give students "tools to think with"—and these are not merely formulas and algorithms. They include concepts and powerful metaphors and heuristic procedures and understanding, including even a determination to acquire an ever deeper understanding of oneself and one's own modes of learning and thinking.

What kinds of experience does school need to provide to children? At the risk of considerable over-simplification, we might list four: (1) the usual "show-and-tell-and-drill" experiences (which, some constructivists admit, may have a limited usefulness—this is another vital area of research: How does drill and practice fit, if it does at all, into a constructivist program?); (2) deliberately created "assimilation paradigms"—that is to say, carefully designed metaphors that correctly mirror the structural features of various pieces of mathematics, and which therefore give the student a basis for powerful mental representations; (3) general background experience, of the type that is sometimes described as "readiness-building" experience; (4) experiences (such as task-based interviews) that give the teacher opportunities to make direct contact with the ways that the student is thinking about some topic or situation or problem. Only the first of these is really familiar in most traditional approaches; here, too, constructivism makes additional demands on its adherents.

Constructivism also requires that we take seriously the meaning of the verb "to abstract"—that is to say, "to scrutinize some messy reality, and somehow draw from it a small skeleton of its most essential features." Long familiar in English schools (and typically neglected in U.S. schools), this means we do not start with formulas for the area of a triangle, or for the perimeter of a circle. Instead, we start with the messy reality of having children measure real "round things" (as in an elegant lesson by Marilyn Burns), and to divide the measured perimeter by the measured diameter, getting something close to the same answer in every case. Our goal is for children to see both states, the messy reality, and the elegant abstraction, and to make the transition from one to the other themselves—a process in which they will need our help and our guidance. Here, again, we see opportunities for research. As Davis pointed out in chapter 7, many of the ideas and techniques used in earlier reforms were sound. Can they be effectively sorted out and incorporated in the new framework? Which of the old "discovery" notions are worth re-examining?

Constructivism also demands of us that we change our approach to teacher education. If learning from experience is important, as constructivists claim, then we need to provide our student teachers with appropriate forms of experience. In constructivist teacher education classes one commonly sees three realities: the reality of mathematics, the reality of humans thinking about mathematics, and the reality of classrooms (that is to say, the reality of human thinking about mathematics in social settings). Thus, one will frequently see student teachers working with one another in small groups, collaborating to solve problems in mathematics, and trying to analyze their own efforts to do so. These will not usually be rote drill, but genuine problems where one does not, at the outset, know how to find a solution. A typical problem might be:

> *In a certain town, two thirds of the adult men are married to three fifths of the adult women. What fraction of the adults in the town are married?*

The purpose of working on such problems is not only to challenge the mathematical thinking of student teachers, although that is important in itself. It is also to invite discussion on how other students might approach such problems, what misconceptions arise and must be corrected, what skills serve as prerequisites for the task, and a host of other pedagogically interesting questions.

The reality of children is often brought into the class via videotapes showing task-based interviews. The reality of classrooms may be brought into the class by films or videotapes showing actual classroom lessons, such as those made by Constance Kamii or by Marilyn Burns. The effort to bring appropriate pieces of reality into teacher education courses is an important aspect of a constructivist approach.

The pedagogical agreement among constructivists is, thus, impressive. But the movement also offers opportunities for fascinating discussion in areas of theoretical disagreement or confusion. Those constructivists who adopt a post-modern stance are raising serious questions about methodology in general. The basic premises of constructivism challenge the long standing hegemony of Cartesian epistemology. Employing Descartes' method, individual thinkers, with all their feelings and intellectual idiosyncrasies, become irrelevant. As Naomi Scheman (1989) says:

> Anyone—so the rationalists and empiricists equally proclaimed—who followed whatever method was recommended would be in a position to know, and what they knew would be the same as what was known by anyone else who followed that same method. Who you were in particular, to whom you were particularly connected, where you were particularly placed, was supposed to make no difference to how things seemed to you—provided, of course, that you were following the prescribed method, the main features of which were designed precisely to insulate your judgment from all these particularities. (p. 41)

Constructivists maintain that all these particularities do matter and that teachers need to understand what their students are trying to do, and with what conceptions they begin. Further, a rejection of universal method means that we as researchers must give up the search for "treatments" designed to replace particular human teachers. Teachers are not synonymous with treatments, and the search for a method that will insulate the classroom from the concrete constructions and personal attributes of teachers and students is a will o' the wisp. There are no valid step-by-step recipes for good teaching any more than there are for good science.

From all of this it should be clear that, whatever else it may be, constructivism is not without consequences. Adopt a constructivist point of view, and you will need to change your expectations of schools, of teachers, of "content," of teacher education, and of research methodologies.

We should also say something about an ethical attitude that must accompany constructivism. We want children to care about mathematics and to care for each other (Noddings, 1984, 1988). To accomplish these goals, we have to care deeply for children. As the poet Goethe said, "We learn best from those we love." Time spent on the development of caring relations between teachers and students is time well spent, and we need to get away from the idea that teachers must spend every minute on instruction driven by precisely stated objectives. Just as "messing around" with mathematical ideas is necessary to mathematical thinking, dialogue is necessary to ethical life and, therefore, to teaching. Children who feel cared for are more likely to engage freely in the kind of intellectual activity we have described here.

Jaime Escalante, the real-life hero of the film *Stand and Deliver*, insists that he must teach his students for three years if they are to succeed in AP calculus. He conscientiously builds relations of care and trust with each student. He shows steady concern for the integral development of his students—how they are doing in English, how their home lives are going, what jobs and sports they participate in. This attitude and the effort that accompanies it are part of teaching mathematics. As we build such relations, our students learn to trust us. When the work is not as exciting as we'd like it to be or when they have low moments (as we all do), students will often persist in mathematical endeavors for their teacher. "Okay, if you say so." "I'll do it—just for you."

Finally, when we open ourselves to caring relations, we learn to listen. Then we become convinced that constructivism is fundamentally right: students do think, and they actively build representations in infinite varieties. They find ideas in working purposively with concrete objects, in talking with each other, in sharing with their teachers. Mathematical growth, like ethical development, is varied and complex; it is under continuous construction and depends, ultimately, on whether students care about mathematics. And that depends, at least in part, on whether we care adequately for them.

REFERENCES

References

Anonymous (1711). *Osservazioni, Giornale de'Letterati d'Italia, 5*(6), 137-140. (Reprinted in Vico, 1858).

Baird, J., & White, R. (1984). *Improving learning through enhanced metacognition: A classroom study*. Paper presented the annual meeting of the American Educational Research Association. New Orleans, LA.

Baroody, A. J. (1985). Mastery of the basic number combinations: Internalization of relationships or facts? *Journal for Research in Mathematics Education, 16*(2), 83-98.

Baroody, A. J. (1987a). *Children's mathematical thinking: A developmental framework for preschool, primary, and special education teachers*. New York: Teachers College Press.

Baroody, A. J. (1987b). The development of counting strategies for single-digit addition. *Journal for Research in Mathematics Education, 18*(2), 141-157.

Baroody, A. J., & Gannon, K. E. (1984). The development of the commutativity principle and economical addition strategies. *Cognition and Instruction, 1*(3), 321-329.

Baroody, A. J., & Ginsburg, H. P. (1986). The relationship between initial meaningful and mechanical knowledge of arithmetic. In J. Hiebert (Ed.), *Conceptual and procedural knowledge: The case of mathematics* (pp. 75-112). Hillsdale, NJ: Lawrence Erlbaum Associates.

Bartlett, F. C. (1932). *Remembering*. Cambridge, England: Cambridge University Press.

Bartlett, F. C. (1958). *Thinking*. New York: Basic Books.

Bauersfeld, H. (1988). Interaction, construction, and knowledge: Alternative perspectives for mathematics education. In T. Cooney & D. Grouws (Eds.), *Effective mathematics teaching* (pp. 27-46). Reston, VA: NCTM.

Biggs, E. (1987). Understanding area. *Journal of Mathematical Behavior, 6* (3), 197-199.

Bishop, A. (1985). The social construction of meaning-a significant development for mathematics education? *For the Learning of Mathematics, 5* (1), 24-28.

Blumer, H. (1969). *Symbolic interactionism*. Englewood Cliffs, NJ: Prentice-Hall.

Bogdanov, A. (1909). Science and philosophy. In (anonymous editor), *Essays on the philosophy of collectivism* (Vol.1). St. Petersburg.

Bridgman, P. (1934). A physicist's second reaction to Mengenlehre. *Scripta Mathematica, 2*, 101-117; 224-234.

Brophy, J. (1986a). Teaching and learning mathematics: Where research should be going. *Journal for Research in Mathematics Education, 17*, 323-346.

Brophy, J. (1986b). What are the data?—A reply to Confrey. *Journal for Research in Mathematics Education, 17*, 361-368.

Brown, J. S., & Burton, R. R. (1978). Diagnostic models for procedural bugs in basic mathematical skills. *Cognitive Science, 2*, 155-192.

Brown, J. S., Collins, A., & Duguid, P. (1989). Situated cognition and the culture of learning. *Educational Researcher, 18* (1), 32-42.

Brown, S. I., & Walter, M. I. (1983). *The art of problem posing*. Philadelphia: The Franklin Institute Press.

Brownell, W. A. (1935). Psychological considerations in the learning and the teaching of mathematics. In D. W. Reeve (Ed.), *The teaching of arithmetic* (Tenth Yearbook of the National Council of Teachers of Mathematics, pp. 1-31). New York: Bureau of Publications, Teachers College, Columbia University.

Brownell, W.A. (1945). When is arithmetic meaningful? *Journal of Educational Research, 38*(7), 481-498.

Bruner, J. (1986). *Actual minds, possible worlds*. Cambridge, MA: Harvard University Press.

Bruni, J.V. (1977). *Experiencing geometry*. Belmont: Wadsworth Publishing Company, Inc.

Burton, L. (1984). Mathematical thinking: The struggle for meaning. *Journal for Research in Mathematics Education, 15*, 321-329.

Bush, W. S. (1986). Preservice teachers' sources of decisions in teaching secondary mathematics. *Journal for Research in Mathematics Education, 17*, 21-30.

Buswell, G. T., & Judd, C. H. (1925). Summary of educational investigations relating to arithmetic. *Supplementary Educational Monographs*, No. 27. Chicago: University of Chicago Press.

Byers, B. (1983). Beyond structure: Some thoughts on the nature of mathematics. In J. C. Bergeron & N. Herscovics (Eds.), *The Proceedings of the Fifth Annual Meeting of PME-NA*, Montreal.

Carpenter, T. P. (1986). Conceptual knowledge as a foundation for procedural knowledge: Implications from research on the initial learning of arithmetic. In J. Hiebert (Ed.), *Conceptual and procedural knowledge: The case of mathematics* (pp. 113-132). Hillsdale, NJ: Lawrence Erlbaum Associates.

Carpenter, T. P., & Fennema, E. (1988). Research and cognitively guided instruction. In E. Fennema, T. P. Carpenter, & S. J. Lamon (Eds.), *Integrating research on teaching and learning mathematics* (pp. 2-19). Madison, WI: Wisconsin Center for Educational Research, University of Wisconsin-Madison.

Carpenter, T. P., Hiebert, J., & Moser, J. M.(1983). The effect of instruction on children's solutions of addition and subtraction word problems. *Educational Studies in Mathematics, 14*, 55-72.

Carpenter, T. P., & Moser, J. M. (1982). The development of addition and subtraction problem-solving skills. In T. P. Carpenter, J. M. Moser, & T. A. Romberg (Eds.),

Addition and subtraction: A cognitive perspective (pp. 9-24). Hillsdale, NJ: Lawrence Erlbaum Associates.

Carpenter, T. P., & Moser, J. M. (1984). The acquisition of addition and subtraction concepts in grades one through three. *Journal for Research in Mathematics Education, 15,* 179-202.

Carpenter, T. P., Moser, J. M., & Romberg, T. A. (Eds.). (1982). *Addition and subtraction: A cognitive perspective.* Hillsdale, NJ: Lawrence Erlbaum Associates.

Chomsky, N. (1968). *Language and mind.* New York: Harcourt Brace Jovanovich.

Chomsky, N. (1971). *Syntactic structures.* The Hague and Paris: Mouton.

Clement, John (1982). Algebra word problem solutions: analysis of a common misconception. *Journal for Research in Mathematics Education, 13,* 16-30.

Cobb, P. (1981). Constructivism, the teaching experiment, and modeling. In C. Comiti and G. Vergnaud (Eds.), *Proceedings of the International Conference of the International Group for the Psychology of Mathematics Education* (Vol. 1, pp. 50-55). Grenoble, France.

Cobb, P. (1985). A reaction to three early number papers. *Journal for Research in Mathematics Education, 16,* 141-145.

Cobb, P. (1988). The tension between theories of learning and theories of instruction in mathematics education. *Educational Psychologist, 23,* 87-104.

Cobb, P. (in press). Multiple perspectives. In L. A. Steffe & T. Wood (Eds.), *Transforming Early Childhood Mathematics Education.* Hillsdale, NJ: Lawrence Erlbaum.

Cobb, P., & Steffe , L. (1983). The constructivist researcher as teacher and model builder. *Journal for Research in Mathematics Education, 14* (2), 83-94.

Cobb, P., & Wheatley, G. (1988). Children's initial understandings of ten. *Focus on Learning Problems in Mathematics, 10* (3), 1-28.

Cobb, P., Wood, T., & Yackel, E. (in press). A constructivist approach to second grade mathematics. In E. von Glasersfeld (Ed.), *Constructivism in mathematics education.* Holland: Reidel.

Cobb, P., Yackel, E., & Wood, T. (1988). Curriculum and teacher development: Psychological and anthropological perspectives. In E. Fennema, T. P. Carpenter, & S. J. Lamon (Eds.), *Integrating research on teaching and learning mathematics* (pp. 92-131). Madison, WI: Wisconsin Center for Educational Research, University of Wisconsin-Madison.

Cobb, P., Yackel, E., & Wood, T. (1989). Young children's emotional acts while doing mathematical problem solving. In D. B. McLeod & V. M. Adams (Eds.), *Affect and mathematical problem solving: A new perspective* (pp. 117-148). New York: Springer-Verlag.

Confrey, J. (1983). *Young women, constructivism and the learning of mathematics.* Paper presented at the annual meeting of the North American Chapter of the International Group for the Psychology of Mathematics Education. Montreal.

Confrey, J. (1985). *A constructivist view of mathematics instruction: A theoretical perspective*. Paper presented at the annual meeting of the American Educational Research Association. Chicago.

Confrey, J. (1986). A critique of teacher effectiveness research in mathematics education. *Journal for Research in Mathematics Education, 17*, 347-360.

Confrey, J. (1987). "Misconceptions" across subject matters: Science, mathematics and programming. *Proceedings of the Second International Seminar on Misconceptions and Educational Strategies in Science and Mathematics, 1*, 81-106. Ithaca, NY: Cornell University.

Cooney, T. (1985). A beginning teacher's view of problem solving. *Journal for Research in Mathematics Education, 16*(5), 324-336.

Cooper, D., & Clancy, M. (1982). *Oh! Pascal!* New York: W.W. Norton & Company.

Crowley, M. L. (1987). The van Hiele model of the development of geometric thought. In M. M. Lindquist & A. P. Shulte (Eds.), *Learning and teaching geometry, K-12* (1987 NCTM Yearbook, pp. 1-16). Reston, VA: National Council of Teachers of Mathematics.

Davis, R. B. (1984). *Learning mathematics: The cognitive approach to mathematics education*. Norwood, NJ: Ablex Publishing Company.

Davis, R. B. (1985a). The role of representations in problem solving: Case studies. *The Journal of Mathematical Behavior, 4*(3), 281-291.

Davis, R. B. (1985b). Solving the "three switch" problem: A case study. *The Journal of Mathematical Behavior, 4*(3), 281-291.

Davis, R. B. (1987). Theory and practice. *The Journal of Mathematical Behavior, 6*, 97-126.

Davis, R. B. (1988a). The world according to McNeill. *Journal of Mathematical Behavior, 7*(1), 51-78.

Davis, R. B. (1988b). The interplay of algebra, geometry, and logic. *Journal of Mathematical Behavior, 7*(1), 9-28

Davis, R. B. (1989). The culture of mathematics and the culture of schools. *The Journal of Mathematical Behavior, 8*(2), 143-160.

Davis, R. B., & McKnight, C. (1980). The influence of semantic content on algorithmic behavior, *Journal of Mathematical Behavior, 3*(1), 39-87.

De Millo, R., Lipton, R., & Perlis, A. (1986). Social processes and proofs of theorems and programs. In T. Tymoczko (Ed.), *New directions in the philosophy of mathematics* (pp. 267-285). Boston: Birkhauser.

Dewey, J. (1938). *Experience and education*. New York: MacMillan.

Dewey, J. (1963). *Experience and education*. New York: Collier.

Diels, H. (1957). *Die Vorsokratiker*. Hamburg: Rowohlt.

Dienes, Z. P. (1963). *An experimental study of mathematics learning*. London: Hutchinson.

Dienes, Z. P. & Jeeves, M. (1965). *Thinking in structures*. London: Hutchinson Educational.

Dilworth, R. P. (1973). The changing face of mathematics education (Final report of the Specialized Teacher Project, 1971-72). Sacramento, California: California State Department of Education.

Dossey, J. A., Mullis, I.V.S., Lindquist, M. M., & Chambers, D. L. (1988). *The mathematics report card: Are we measuring up?* (National Assessment of Educational Progress report). Princeton: Educational Testing Service.

Doyle, W., Sanford, J. & Emmer, E. (1983). *Managing academic tasks in junior high school: Background, design and methodology* (Report No. 6185). Austin: University of Texas, Research and Development Center for Teacher Education.

Erlwanger, S. H. (1973). Benny's conception of rules and answers in IPI mathematics. *Journal of Children's Mathematical Behavior, 1*(2), 7-26.

Erlwanger, S. H. (1975). Case studies of children's conceptions of mathematics, part I. *Journal of Children's Mathematical Behavior, 1*(3), 157-283.

Fabricus, W. (1979). Piaget's theory of knowledge; Its philosophical context. *High/Scope Report, 4*(7), 4-13.

Fennema, E., Carpenter, T. P, & Peterson, P. (1986). *Teachers' decision making and cognitively guided instruction: A new paradigm for curriculum development*. Paper presented at the seventh annual meeting of the International Group for the Psychology of Mathematics Education. London, England.

Feyerabend, P. (1987). *Farewell to reason*. London/New York: Verso.

Forman, G., & Pufall, P. B. (Eds.) (1988). *Constructivism in the computer age*. Hillsdale, NJ: Lawrence Erlbaum.

Fuson, K. C. (1988). *Children's counting and concepts of number*. New York: Springer-Verlag.

Fuson, K. C., & Hall, J. W. (1983). The acquisition of early number word meanings: A conceptual analysis and review. In H. P. Ginsburg (Ed.), *The development of mathematical thinking* (pp. 49-107). New York: Academic Press.

Gelman, R., & Gallistel, C. (1978). *Young children's understanding of numbers*. Cambridge: Harvard University Press.

Ginsburg, H. P. (1977). *Children's arithmetic: The learning process*. New York, NY: Van Nostrand.

Ginsburg, H. P. (1982). *Children's arithmetic: How they learn it and how you teach it*. Austin, TX: Pro-Ed.

Ginsburg, H. P. (1983). *The development of mathematical thinking*. New York: Academic Press.

Ginsburg, H. P. (1989). *Children's arithmetic* (2nd ed.). Austin, TX: Pro-Ed.

Ginsburg, H. P. , & Oper, S. (Eds.). (1969) *Piaget's theory of intellectual development.* Englewood Cliffs, N.J.: Prentice-Hall.

Ginsburg, H. P., Posner, J. K., & Russell, R. L. (1981). The development of mental addition as a function of schooling. *Journal of Cross-Cultural Psychology, 12,* 163-178.

Ginsburg, H. P., & Russell, R. L. (1981). Social class and racial influences on early mathematical thinking. *Monographs of the Society for Research in Child Development, 46*:(16) (Serial No. 193).

Goldin, G. A. (1984). Structure variables in problem solving. In G. A. Goldin and C. E. McClintock (Eds.), *Task variables in mathematical problem solving* (pp 103-169). Philadelphia: Franklin Institute Press (presently Hillsdale, New Jersey: Lawrence Erlbaum Associates).

Goldin, G. A. (1987). Cognitive representational systems for mathematical problem solving. In C. Janvier (Ed.), *Problems of representation in the teaching and learning of mathematics* (pp. 125-145). Hillsdale, New Jersey: Lawrence Erlbaum Associates.

Goldin, G. A. (1989). Constructivist epistemology and discovery learning in mathematics. In G. Vergnaud, J. Rogalski, & M. Artigue (Eds.), *Actes de la 13e Conference Internationale de PME (International Group for the Psychology of Mathematics Education)* (Vol. 2, pp 15-22). Paris.

Good, T. L., & Grouws, D. A. (1978). *Missouri mathematics effectiveness project: A program of naturalistic and experimental research* (Tech. Report No. 142). Columbia: University of Missouri, Center for Research in Social Behavior.

Good, T. L., Grouws, D. A., & Ebmeier, H. (1983). *Active mathematics teaching*. New York: Longman.

Groen, G. J., & Resnick, L. B. (1977). Can preschool children invent addition algorithms? *Journal of Educational Psychology, 69,* 645-652.

Gunstone, R., & Northfield, J. (1988, April). *Inservice education: Some constructivist perspectives and examples*. Paper presented at the annual meeting of the American Educational Research Association. New Orleans.

Guskey, T. R. (1986). Staff development and the process of teacher change. *Educational Researcher, 15*(5), 5-12.

Hadamard, J. (1945). *The psychology of invention in the mathematical field.* New York: Dover Publications, Inc.

Hare-Mustin, R. T., & Marecek, J. (1988). The meaning of difference. *American Psychologist, 43*, 455-464.

Harlen, W., & Osborne, R. (1985). A model for learning and teaching applied to primary science. *Journal of Curriculum Studies, 17*(2), 133-146.

Hiebert, J. (1984). Children's mathematics learning: The struggle to link form and understanding. *Elementary School Journal, 84,* 497-513.

Hiebert, J. (Ed.). (1986). *Conceptual and procedural knowledge: The case of mathematics.* Hillsdale, NJ: Lawrence Erlbaum Associates.

Holt, J. (1964). *How children fail.* New York: Delta Books.

Howson, G. C. J., Keitel, C., & Kilpatrick, J. (1981). *Curriculum development in mathematics.* Cambridge, England: Cambridge University Press.

Inhelder, B., Garcia, R., & Voneche, J. (1977). *Epistemologie genetique et equilibration.* Neuchatel/Paris: Delachauz et Niestle.

James, W. (1880). Great men, great thoughts, and the environment. *Atlantic Monthly, 46,* 441-459.

Kamii, C. K. (1985). *Young children reinvent arithmetic.* New York: Teachers College Press.

Kelly, G. A. (1955). *A theory of personality: The psychology of personal constructs.* New York: Norton.

Kidder, T. (1989). *Among schoolchildren.* Boston: Houghton Mifflin.

Kilpatrick, J. (1986). Reflection and recursion. In Carss, M. (Ed.), *Proceedings of the Fifth International Congress on Mathematical Education.* Boston: Birkhauser.

Kilpatrick, J. (1987). What constructivism might be in mathematics education. In J. C. Bergeron, N. Herscovics & C. Kieran (Eds.), *Proceedings of the Eleventh Conference of the International Group for the Psychology of Mathematics Education* (pp. 2-27). Montreal: University of Montreal.

Kintsch, W. & Greeno, J. G. (1985). Understanding and solving arithmetic word problems. *Psychological Review, 92,* 109-129.

Kitchener, R. (1989). Genetic epistemology and the prospects for a cognitive sociology of science: A critical synthesis. *Social Epistemology, 3*(2), 153-169.

Kline, M. (1980). *Mathematics: The loss of certainty.* New York: Oxford University Press.

Koretz, D. (1988). Arriving in Lake Wobegon: Are standardized tests exaggerating achievement and distorting instruction? *American Educator, 12*(2), 8-52.

Kouba, V. (1986, April). *How young children solve multiplication and division word problems.* Paper presented at the National Council of Teachers of Mathematics research presession, Washington, D.C.

Labinowicz, E. (1985). *Learning from children: New beginnings for teaching numerical thinking.* Menlo Park, CA: Addison-Wesley.

Labinowicz, E. (1987). Children's right to be wrong. *Arithmetic Teacher, 35*(4), 2 & 20.

Lakatos, I. (1976). *Proofs and refutations* (J. Worral & E. Zahar, Eds.). Cambridge: Cambridge University Press.

Lampert, M. (1988). The teacher's role in reinventing the meaning of mathematical knowing in the classroom. *Proceedings of the North America Chapter of the Psychology of Mathematics Education Group* (pp. 433-480). Northern Illinois University.

Landis, J. H. (1990). *Teachers' prediction and identification of children's mathematical behavior: Two case studies*. Unpublished doctoral dissertation. Rutgers University.

Landis, J. H. and Maher, C. A. (1989). Observations of Carrie, a fourth grade student, doing mathematics. *The Journal of Mathematical Behavior, 8*(1), 3-12.

Lave, J. (1988). *Cognition in practice: Mind, mathematics and culture in everyday life.* Cambridge: Cambridge University Press.

Lawler, R. W. (in press). Constructing knowledge from interactions. *Journal of Mathematical Behavior.*

Lerman, S. (1989). Constructivism, mathematics, and mathematics education. *Educational Studies in Mathematics, 20*, 211-223.

Lesh, R., & Landau, M. (Eds.). (1983). *Acquisition of mathematical concepts and processes.* New York: Academic Press.

Lesh, R., & Zawojewski, J. (1987). Problem solving. In T. Post (Ed.), *Teaching mathematics in grades K-8: Research-based methods.* Boston: Allyn & Bacon.

Lochhead, J. (1983a). *Beyond Emile.* Paper presented at the annual meeting of the American Educational Research Association. Montreal.

Lochhead, J. (1983b). Constructivist approach to teaching mathematics. In J. C. Bergeron & N. Herscovics (Eds.), *Proceedings of the Fifth Annual Meeting: PME/NA.*

Lortie, D. C. (1975). *School teacher.* Chicago: University of Chicago Press.

Lunkenbein, D. (1985, April). *Cognitive structures underlying processes and conceptions in geometry.* Paper presented at the research presession of the annual meeting of the National Council of Teachers of Mathematics. San Antonio, TX.

Mager, R. (1962). *Preparing instructional objectives.* Palo Alto, California: Fearon.

Magoon, A. J. (1977). Constructivist approaches in educational research. *Review of Educational Research, 47*(4), 651-693.

Maher, C. A. (1986, June). *Teacher development in mathematics: A model.* Paper presented at the working conference on Models for Teacher Development. Rutgers University.

Maher, C. A., & Alston, A. (1988, July). *Implementing a model for teacher development in mathematics.* Paper presented to the Sixth International Congress on Mathematical Education. Budapest, Hungary.

Maher, C. A., and Alston, A. (1989). Is meaning connected to symbols? An interview with Ling Chen. *The Journal of Mathematical Behavior, 8*(3), 241-248.

Maturana, H. (1980a). Biology and cognition. In H. Maturana & F. Varela (Eds.), *Autopoiesis: The organization of the living*. Dordrecht: Reidel.

Maturana, H. R. (1980b). Man and society. In F. Benseler, P. M. Hejl, & W. K. Kock (Eds.), *Antopoiesis, communication, and society* (pp. 11-32). Frankfurt, West Germany: Campus Verlag.

McKnight, C. (1987). *The underachieving curriculum.* Champaign: Stipes Publishing Company.

McKnight, C. C., Crosswhite, F. J., Dossey, J. A., Kifer, E., Swafford, S. D. Travers, K. J., Cooney, T. J. (1987). *The underachieving curriculum: Assessing U.S. school mathematics from an international perspective.* Champaign, IL: Stipes.

McNeill, R. (1988). A reflection on when I loved math, and how I stopped. *Journal of Mathematical Behavior,* 7(1), 45-50.

Mead, G. H. (1934). *Mind, self, and society.* Chicago, IL: University of Chicago Press.

Montaigne, Michel de (1972). *Essais* (Vol.2). Paris: Librairie Generale Francaise.

Moyer, M. B., & Moyer, J. C. (1985). Ensuring that practice makes perfect: Implications for children with learning difficulties. *Arithmetic Teacher, 33*(1), 40-42.

NACOME. (1975). *Overview and analysis of school mathematics, Grades K-12.* Washington, DC: Conference Board of the Mathematical Sciences.

National Council of Teachers of Mathematics. (1989). *Curriculum and evaluation standards for school mathematics.* Reston, VA: NCTM, Inc.

National Research Council. (1989). *Everybody counts: A report to the nation on the future of mathematics education.* Washington, DC: National Academy Press.

Neisser, U. (1967). *Cognitive psychology.* New York: Appleton-Century-Crofts.

Nicholls, J. G. (1983). Conceptions of ability and achievement motivation: A theory and its implications for education. In S. G. Paris, G. M. Olson, & W. H. Stevenson (Eds.), *Learning and motivation in the classroom* (pp. 211-237). Hillsdale, NJ: Lawrence Erlbaum Associates.

Nicholls, J. G. (1989). *The competitive ethos and democratic education.* Cambridge: Harvard University Press.

Noddings, N. (1973). *Constructivism as a base for a theory of teaching.* Unpublished doctoral dissertation, Stanford University.

Noddings, N. (1974). Competence theories and the science of education. *Educational Theory, 24*, 356-364.

Noddings, N. (1984). *Caring: A feminine approach to ethics and moral education.* Berkeley: University of California Press.

Noddings, N. (1986). *Teaching as a heuristic enterprise.* Paper presented at the annual meeting of the Psychology of Mathematics Education Group. East Lansing, Michigan.

Noddings, N. (1988). An ethic of caring and its implications for instructional arrangements. *American Journal of Education, 96*(2), 215-230.

Noddings, N. (1989). Theoretical and practical concerns about small groups in mathematics. *The Elementary School Journal, 89*(5), 607-623.

Novak, J., & Gowin, D. B. (1984). *Learning how to learn.* New York: Cambridge University Press.

Nussbaum, J. (1982). Alternative frameworks, conceptual conflict and accommodation: Toward a principled teaching strategy. *Instructional Science, 11*, 183-200.

Osborne, R., Bell, B., & Gilbert, J. (1982). *Science teaching and children's view of the world.* Hamilton, New Zealand: S.E.R.U., University of Waikato.

Papert, S. (1980). *Mindstorms: Children, computers, and powerful ideas.* New York: Basic Books.

Perret-Clermont, A. N. (1980). *Social interaction and cognitive development in children.* New York: Academic Press.

Perry, M., Church, R., & Goldin-Meadow, S. (1988, April). *Learning a principle versus learning a procedure: Looking beyond what is taught.* Paper presented at the annual meeting of the American Educational Research Association, New Orleans.

Peterson, P., & Clark C. (1978). Teachers' reports of their cognitive processes during teaching. *American Educational Research Journal, 14*(4), 555-565.

Peterson, P., Swing, S., Stark, K., & Waas, C. (1984). Students' cognitions and time on task during mathematics instruction. *American Educational Research Journal, 21*(3), 487-515.

Piaget, J. (1937). *La construction du reel chez l'enfant.* Neuchatel: Delachaux et Niestle.

Piaget, J. (1948). *To understand is to invent.* New York: Viking.

Piaget, J. (1953). *Logic and psychology.* Manchester, England: Manchester University Press.

Piaget, J. (1964). Learning and development. In R. E. Ripple, & V. N. Rockcastle (Eds.), *Piaget rediscovered* (Report of the Conference on Cognitive Studies and Curriculum Development). Ithaca, NY: Cornell University.

Piaget, J. (1965). *The child's conception of number.* New York: Norton.

Piaget, J. (1969). *Mechanisms of perception* (G. N. Seagrim, Trans.). New York: Basic Books.

Piaget, J. (1970a). *Genetic epistemology.* New York: Columbia University Press.

Piaget, J. (1970b). *Le structuralisme.* Paris: Presses Universitaires de France.

Piaget, J. (1970c). *Science of education and the psychology of the child.* New York: Orion.

Piaget, J. (1970d). *Structuralism.* New York: Basic Books.

Piaget, J. (1971a). *Biology and knowledge.* Chicago: University of Chicago Press.

Piaget, J. (1971b). *Insights and illusions of philosophy.* New York: World.

Piaget, J. (1980a). *Adaptation and intelligence: Organic selection and phenocopy.* Chicago: University of Chicago Press.

Piaget, J. (1980b). Afterthoughts. In M. Piattelli-Palmarine (Ed.), *Language and learning: The debate between Jean Piaget and Noam Chomsky.* Cambridge: Harvard University Press.

Piaget, J. (1980c). The psychogenesis of knowledge and its epistemological significance. In M. Piattelli-Palmarini (Ed.), *Language and learning: The debate between Jean Piaget and Noam Chomsky.* Cambridge: Harvard University Press.

Piattelli-Palmarini, M. (1980). How hard is the "hard core" of a scientific program? In M. Piattelli-Palmarini (Ed.), *Language and Learning: The debate between Jean Piaget and Noam Chomsky.* Cambridge: Harvard University Press.

Pierce, C. S. (1935). *Collected papers of Charles Sanders Pierce* (Vol. 5, C. Hartshorne & P. Weiss, Eds.). Cambridge: Harvard University Press.

Pittendrigh, C. S. (1958). Adaptation, natural selection, and behavior. In A. Roe & G. G. Simpson (Eds.), *Behavior and evolution.* New Haven, CT: Yale University Press.

Plato. (1956). *Great dialogues of Plato.* New York: New American Library.

Polya, G. (1962). *Mathematical discovery: On understanding, learning, and teaching problem solving.* New York: John Wiley & Sons, Inc.

Popkin, R. (1979). *The history of scepticism from Erasmus to Spinoza.* Berkeley/Los Angeles: University of California Press.

Quine, W. V. O. (1969). Epistemology naturalized. In W. V. O. Quine (Ed.), *Ontological relativity and other essays.* New York: Columbia University Press.

Resnick, L. B. (1983). A developmental theory of number understanding. In H. P. Ginsburg (Ed.), *The development of mathematical thinking* (pp. 109-151). New York: Academic Press.

Resnick, L. B., & Ford, W. W. (1981). *The psychology of mathematics for instruction.* Hillsdale, NJ: Lawrence Erlbaum Associates.

Reyes, L. H. (1984). Affective variables and mathematics education. *Elementary School Journal, 84*, 558-581.

Riley, M. S., Greeno, J. G., & Heller, J. I. (1983). Development of children's problem-solving ability in arithmetic. In H. P. Ginsburg (Ed.), *The development of mathematical thinking* (pp. 153-200). New York: Academic Press.

Rogoff, B., & Lave, J. (Eds.) (1984). *Everyday cognition: Its development in social context.* Cambridge: Harvard University Press.

Rorty, R. (1979). *Philosophy and the mirror of nature.* Princeton: Princeton University Press.

Rosenshine, B. (1976). Classroom instruction. In N. Gage (Ed.), *The psychology of teaching methods* (Seventy-seventh Yearbook, pp. 335-371). Chicago: National Society for the Study of Education.

Ross, S. (1986, April). *The development of children's place-value numeration concepts in grades two through five.* Paper presented at the annual meeting of the American Educational Research Association. San Francisco, CA.

Rowell, J.A. (1989). Equilibration and the teaching of science. *Synthese, 80*(1), 141-162.

Scheman, N. (1989). Commentary on Sandra Harding's "The method question." *Newsletter on Feminism and Philosophy, 88*(3), 40-44.

Schoenfeld, A. H. (1985). *Mathematical problem solving.* New York: Academic Press.

Schoenfeld, A. H. (1987). What's all the fuss about metacognition? In A. H. Schoenfeld (Ed.), *Cognitive science and mathematics education* (pp. 189-216). Hillsdale, NJ: Lawrence Erlbaum Associates.

Schoenfeld, A. H., Smith, J. P., & Arcavi, A. (in press). Learning: The microgenetic analysis of one student's evolving understanding of complex subject matter domain. In R. Glaser (Ed.), *Advances in instructional psychology* (Vol. 4). Hillsdale, NJ: Lawrence Erlbaum Associates.

Schon, D. A. (1983). *The reflective practitioner.* New York: Basic Books.

Schutz, A. (1962). *The problem of social reality.* The Hague, Holland: Martinus Nijhoff.

Siegel, H. (1988). Rationality and epistemic dependence. *Educational Philosophy and Theory, 20*(1), 1-6.

Siegler, R. S. (1987). Strategy choices in subtraction. In J. Slobada & D. Rogers (Eds.), *Cognitive process in mathematics* (pp. 81-106). Oxford, England; Oxford University Press.

Siegler, R. S., & Shrager, J. (1984). Strategy choices in addition: How do children know what to do? In C. Sophian (Ed.), *Origins of cognitive skills* (pp. 229-293). Hillsdale, NJ: Lawrence Erlbaum Associates.

Simmel, G. (1885). Ueber eine Beziehung der Selectionslehre zur Erkenntnistheorie. *Archiv fur systematische Philosophie, 1*, 34-45.

Simon, H. (1979). *Models of thought.* New Haven: Yale University Press.

Skinner, B. F. (1953). *Science and Human Behavior.* New York: The Free Press.

Slobin, D. I. (1971). *Psycholinguistics*. Glenview, IL: Scott, Foresman.

Smedslund, J. (1977). Piaget's psychology in practice. *British Journal of Educational Psychology, 47*, 1-6.

Snow, R. (1972). *A model teacher training system: An overview* (Research and Development Memorandum 92, Ed. 066 437). Stanford: Center for the Research and Development in Teaching.

Starkey, P., & Gelman, R. (1982). The development of addition and subtraction abilities prior to formal schooling in arithmetic. In T. P. Carpenter, J. M. Moser, & T. A. Romberg (Eds.), *Addition and subtraction: A cognitive perspective* (pp. 99-116). Hillsdale, NJ: Lawrence Erlbaum Associates.

Steffe, L. P.(1983). The teaching experiment methodology in a constructivist research program. In M. Zweng, T. Green, J. Kilpatrick, H. Pollak, & M. Suydam (Eds.), *Proceedings of the Fourth International Congress on Mathematical Education* (pp. 469-471). Boston: Birkhauser.

Steffe, L. P. (1986, April). *Mathematical teacher education in a constructivist framework.* Paper presented at the annual meeting of the American Educational Research Association, San Francisco.

Steffe, L. P. (1987, April). *Principles of mathematical curriculum design in early childhood teacher education.* Paper presented at the annual meeting of the American Educational Research Association. Washington, DC.

Steffe, L. P. (1988, April). *Mathematics learning and teaching for today's schools.* Paper presented at the annual meeting of the National Council for the Teachers of Mathematics. Chicago.

Steffe, L. P., & Cobb, P. (1983). The constructivist researcher as teacher and model builder. *Journal for Research in Mathematics Education, 14*, 83-94.

Steffe, L. P., Cobb, P., & von Glasersfeld, E. (1988). *Construction of arithmetical meanings and strategies.* New York: Springer-Verlag.

Steffe, L. P., von Glasersfeld, E., Richards, J., & Cobb, P. (1983). *Children's counting types: Philosophy, theory, and applications.* New York: Praeger Scientific.

Steffe, L. P., Shrum, J. W., Clifton, P. D. Hart, N., & Ireland, E. K. (1985). Final report: Secretary's discretionary program, planning grant to develop the Georgia Teacher Fellow Program in Science and Mathematics. In A. Buccino & C. Purvis (Eds.). *Designing and implementing a teacher career ladder.* Athens: The Clarke County (Georgia) Schools and The College of Education of the University of Georgia.

Stephens, W., & Romberg T. (1985). *Reconceptualizing the role of the mathematics teacher.* Paper presented at the Annual Meeting of the American Educational Research Association. Chicago.

Stevens, A. L., & Collins, A. (1980). Multiple conceptual models of a complex system. In R. E. Snow, P. Federica, & W. E. Montague (Eds.), *Aptitude, learning and instruction: Cognitive process analyses of learning and problem solving* (Vol. 2, pp. 177-188). Hillsdale, NJ: Lawrence Erlbaum Associates.

Sund, R., & Picard, A. (1972). *Behavioral objectives and evaluational measures: Science and mathematics*. Columbus, Ohio: Merrill.

Thom, R. (1973). Modern mathematics: Does it exist? In Howson, A.G. (Ed.), *Developments in mathematical education: Proceedings of the Second International Congress on Mathematical Education* (pp. 194-209). Cambridge: Cambridge University Press.

Thompson, P. (1985). Experience, problem solving, and learning mathematics: Considerations in developing mathematical curricula. In E. A. Silver (Ed.), *Teaching and learning mathematical problem solving: Multiple research perspectives* (pp. 189-236). Hillsdale, NJ: Lawrence Erlbaum Associates.

Thoresen, C. (1988). The constructivist concept: Primacy of the obscure. *The Counseling Psychologist, 16*(2), 249-255.

Toulmin, S. (1972). *Human understanding* (Vol. 1). Princeton: Princeton University Press.

Turner, M. (1967). *Philosophy and the science of behavior*. New York: Appleton-Century-Crofts.

Vaihinger, H. (1913). *Die Philosophie des Als Ob*. Berlin: Reuther & Reichard.

Van Engen, H. (1949). Analysis of meaning in arithmetic. *Elementary School Journal. 49*, 321-329; 335-400.

Vico, G. B. (1858). *De antiquissima Italorum sapientia* (1710) . Naples: Stamperia de'Classici Latini.

Vinner, S. (1983). Concept definition, concept image, and the notion of function. *International Journal for Mathematics Education, Science and Technology, 14*(3), 293-305.

Voigt, J. (1985). Patterns and routines in classroom interaction. *Researches en didactique des mathematiques, 6*, 69-118.

von Glasersfeld, E. (1974). *Piaget and the radical constructivist epistemology*. Paper presented at the Third Southeastern Conference of the Society for Research on Child Development. Chapel Hill, NC.

von Glasersfeld, E. (1980). Adaptation and viability. *American Psychologist, 35*(11), 970-974.

von Glasersfeld, E. (1981). The "truth" about Pythagoras. *Problem Solving. 3*(5 & 6).

von Glasersfeld, E. (1982). Subitizing: The role of figural patterns in the development of numerical concepts. *Archives de Psychologie. 50*, 191-218.

von Glasersfeld, E. (1983). On the concept of interpretation. *Poetics, 12,* 207-218.

von Glasersfeld, E. (1984). An introduction to radical constructivism. In P. Watzlawick (Ed.), *The invented reality* (pp. 17-40). New York: Norton.

von Glasersfeld, E. (1985). Reconstructing the concept of knowledge. *Archives de Psychologie, 53,* 91-101.

von Glasersfeld, E. (1987a). Learning as a constructive activity. In C. Janvier (Ed.), *Problems of representation in the teaching and learning of mathematics* (pp. 3-17). Hillsdale, NJ: Lawrence Erlbaum Associates.

von Glasersfeld, E. (1987b). Preliminaries to any theory of representation. In C. Janvier (Ed.), *Problems of representation in the teaching and learning of mathematics* (pp. 215-225). Hillsdale, New Jersey: Lawrence Erlbaum Associates.

von Glasersfeld, E. (1988, July). *Environment and communication.* Paper presented at the Sixth International Congress on Mathematical Education. Budapest, Hungary.

von Glasersfeld, E. (in press). Abstraction, re-presentation, and reflection. In L. P. Steffe (Ed.), *Epistemological foundations of mathematical experience.* New York: Springer-Verlag.

von Uexkiill, J. (1970). *Streifziige durch die Umwelten von Tieren und Menschen* (with Georg Kriszat). Frankfurt am Main: Fischer. (Originally published in 1933).

Vuyk, R. (1981). *Overview and critique of Piaget's genetic epistemology* (Vols. 1 & 2). New York: Academic Press.

Vygotsky, L. S. (1962). *Thought and language.* Cambridge, MA.: M.I.T. Press.

Vygotsky, L. S. (1978). *Mind in society: The development of higher psychological processes.* Cambridge, MA: Harvard University Press.

Weber, R. (1986, April). *The constraints of questioning routines in reading instruction.* Paper presented at the meeting of American Educational Research Association. San Francisco, CA.

Wertheimer, M. (1959). *Productive thinking* (Enlarged edition). New York: Harper & Row.

Wertsch, J. V. (1985). *Vygotsky and the social formation of mind.* Cambridge: Harvard University Press.

Whimbey, A., & Lochhead J. (1980). *Problem solving and comprehension.* Philadelphia: Franklin Institute Press.

Whitney, H. (1985). Taking responsibility in school mathematics education, *The Journal of Mathematical Behavior, 4*(3), 219-235.

Wittgenstein, L. (1961). *Tractatus logico-philosophicus.* London: Routledge & Kegan Paul.

Wittgenstein, L. (1964). *Remarks on the foundations of mathematics.* Oxford: Blackwell.

Wood, T. (in press). Whole class interactions as the negotiation of social contexts within which to construct mathematical knowledge. In C. Keitel (Ed.), *Mathematics, education and society.* Berlin: UNESCO.

Wood, T., Cobb, P., & Yackel, E. (in press). The contextual nature of teaching: Mathematics and reading instruction in one second-grade classroom. *Elementary School Journal.*

Woods, S. S., Resnick, L. B., & Groen, G. J. (1975). An experimental test of five process models for subtraction. *Journal of Educational Psychology, 67,* 17-21.